Cooperative Learning in Math

by
Bob Bernstein

illustrated by Bron Smith

Cover by Bron Smith

Good Apple, Inc.
299 Jefferson Road
P.O. Box 480
Parsippany, NJ 07054-0480

SIMON & SCHUSTER *A Paramount Communications Company*

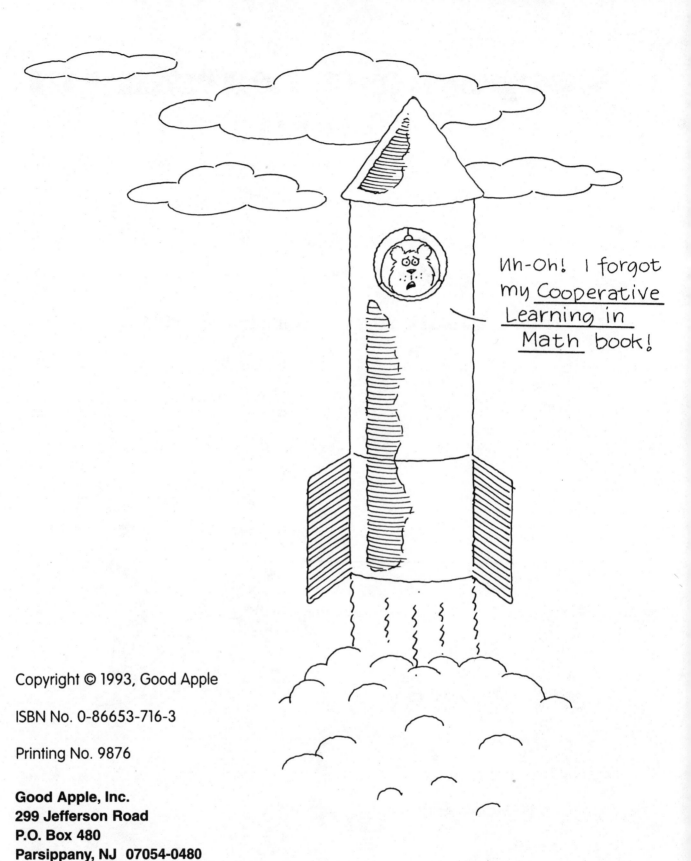

Copyright © 1993, Good Apple

ISBN No. 0-86653-716-3

Printing No. 9876

Good Apple, Inc.
299 Jefferson Road
P.O. Box 480
Parsippany, NJ 07054-0480

Dedication

This book is dedicated to friends . . . .

An old friend who is young and fresh with spirit and wisdom . . .
A friend of mine since our first days in high school . . .
      my friend Lowell Fishman

And . . . a new friend . . . the kind of friend teachers need to maintain their balance throughout the course of a school year. I met this friend while teaching his first grade class. He is now in second grade . . .
      my friend Ian Baylis

              Thanks for everything.
                  Bob

Table of Contents

I can't see the TABLE of CONTENTS — without my glasses!

GA1433

Introduction

Cooperative learning is an environment that encourages a complete and total involvement in the learning process. It is this kind of exposure that lends itself to the improvement of a student's attitude and outlook with regard to his/her ability to learn. Not only is each student a unique source of information, but he or she is encouraged to share such expertise with fellow classmates.

Participants in cooperative learning will become involved with situations that incorporate important life skills such as communication (allowing students an opportunity to learn how to listen, how to think and then how they might approach problem solving). Instead of having to respond as someone in the classroom who is not sure of his/her ability or even someone who might be quite sure of his/her ability with a particular topic, students are encouraged to be a teacher, to become an active learner to offer and to share ideas and to interact with all group members and classmates. It is important to assume responsibility for finding ways of reaching a successful conclusion to a problem. Praise (when warranted) will encourage sharing strategies and thinking processes.

The activities that are presented in this book are designed to encourage students to reach out to help and to learn from one another. Students who might feel a strength in one particular area of mathematics will learn to respect other students who have particular strengths in still other areas of mathematics, in other words, the development of mutual respect and mutual admiration.

Cooperative learning is working, learning, sharing and thinking. It is groups and classes striving for success and the winning attitude. It is also students who tend to encourage guessing and exploration of problems. This book places a strong emphasis on varied experiences in problem solving so as to investigate math content, to develop strategies, to interpret results and finally, to be able to generalize solutions in a meaningful way. We all want our students to feel confident when dealing with mathematics.

To better ease into and facilitate the classroom learning experience, it is the responsibility of the instructional leader to clearly and effectively state the objective of each lesson. The teacher who sets attainable goals also allows his/her students many opportunities to experience success. This is a process that can be more easily attained by the teacher's careful placement of youngsters into groups that will be conducive to learning.

Before presenting these activities and ideas to students, a teacher should read them, try them and get a feel for them. It is when directions are clear and explicit at the outset that learning has an excellent beginning.

As the groups begin to develop various strategies, as they begin to share expertise or even as they show a need for more direction, it is still the teacher who is walking around the room, who is looking, listening and offering guidance. Finally, it is the instructor who must monitor each student's strengths and weaknesses through all of this intergroup interaction.

Poems

SKILLS: Problem Solving
       Computational

The poems on the following pages are challenging. Group members should read each poem carefully, and then discuss all of the questions with team members.

Carefully review and consider the reasons offered by each individual when arriving at a recorded answer.

After using the allotted time to solve the problem, be ready to share answers with your classmates.

GA1433

Names _____

Poems

There were 50 geese perched high on the wall
When 26 of them had a great fall.
$1/2$ of those left were sitting quite proud;
It was they who managed to honk most loud.
Of those that remained silent, $1/4$ flew away
And $1/3$ of that group landed in the bay.

Questions:
1. How many geese remained perched on the wall? _____
2. How many geese were sitting quite proud? _____
3. How many geese flew away?_____
4. How many geese landed in the bay?_____

Share your answers with other other groups. Do they all agree with you?

School Yard

18 children were in the school yard at play;

$1/3$ of them had nothing to say.

Of those that did talk,

$2/3$ took a walk,

And $1/2$ of those walking wore very little gray.

Questions:

1. How many children had nothing to say? _____

2. How many children did talk?_____

3. How many children took a walk? _____

4. How many children wore very little gray? _____

GA1433

The Mystery Book

On Monday I had money set aside to buy a book.
It was then that I discovered it was not enough cash I took.

On Tuesday I doubled the money I originally had.
Again only to find out I was short, . . . how sad.

On Wednesday I managed to triple my loot from the previous day.
I thought for sure the book will be mine as I went on my way , . . .
  how sad.

I still did not have enough to meet the book's cost.
My hopes were dashed on Thursday. I felt lost.

And then came Friday and I am now able to say . . .
I found an additional $1/2$ of the monies that I had yesterday.

And so Thursday's total and Friday's find
Allowed this great book to be mine.

P.S. On Tuesday I had $2.40.

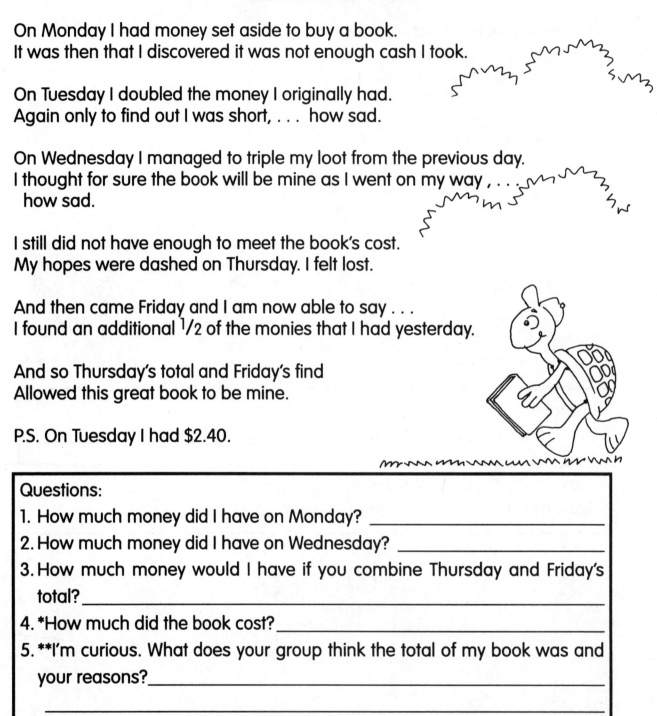

Questions:
1. How much money did I have on Monday? _____
2. How much money did I have on Wednesday? _____
3. How much money would I have if you combine Thursday and Friday's total? _____
4. *How much did the book cost? _____
5. **I'm curious. What does your group think the total of my book was and your reasons? _____

_____

GA1433

How Many Animals in My Zoo? I'll Tell You!

In our zoo you'll find 7 pairs of cockatoos.

There are 9 zebras striped black and white
And a dozen tigers looking for something to bite.

You will see 87 exotic birds with magnificent plumage galore
Plus 3^1/$_2$ dozen smaller birds, many of whom lived on the shore.

We have ^{1}/$_2$ dozen alligators . . . in the water all day they lie,
While staring at the crocodiles slowly swimming by.

By the way, our zoo has but 9 crocs,
And their home seems to be in the shallow rocks.

A dozen gorillas and 9 chimpanzees
Can always be spotted near gracious old trees . . .

Eating bananas, their choice for the day.
It's also our rhino's pick, not hay.

Please don't forget our 5 elephants so strong . . .
Nor our 6 giraffes with necks that are most long.

There are 7 huge bears gigantic in size and
1 glorious lion, our zoo's valued prize.

How many animals in my zoo?

Our answer _____

Our reasons _____

_____

_____

_____

_____

Cross Out Something

SKILLS: Problem Solving
           Computational

This project presents a problem for your group's consideration. Examine the following . . . a series of numbers whose sum is $\boxed{21}$.

$$1 + 2 + 3 + 4 + 5 + 6 = \boxed{21}$$

If you cross out one number in this series, the remaining numbers when added together will have a sum of $\boxed{16}$. Which of the above numbers is to be crossed out?

After some discussion your group will cross out the 5.

$$1 + 2 + 3 + 4 + \cancel{5} + 6 = \boxed{16}$$

Another example:
The sum of the numbers in this series is $\boxed{52}$.

$$3 + 4 + 5 + 6 + 7 + 8 + 9 + 10 = \boxed{52}$$

Cross out one number so that the sum will be $\boxed{45}$.

$$3 + 4 + 5 + 6 + \cancel{7} + 8 + 9 + 10 = \boxed{45}$$

And still another example:
The sum of the numbers in this series is $\boxed{84}$.

$$6 + 8 + 10 + 12 + 14 + 16 + 18 = \boxed{84}$$

Cross out two numbers so that the sum will be $\boxed{62}$.

$$6 + 8 + \cancel{10} + \cancel{12} + 14 + 16 + 18 = \boxed{62}$$

GA1433

Names _____

Cross Out Something

A. The sum of the numbers in this series is $\boxed{48}$.

$$3 + 5 + 7 + 9 + 11 + 13 = \boxed{48}$$

Cross out one number so that the sum will be $\boxed{37}$.

$$3 + 5 + 7 + 9 + 11 + 13 = \boxed{37}$$

The cross-out number is $\boxed{}$.

B. The sum of the numbers in this series is $\boxed{129}$.

$$19 + 20 + 21 + 22 + 23 + 24 = \boxed{129}$$

Cross out one number so that the sum will be $\boxed{108}$.

$$19 + 20 + 21 + 22 + 23 + 24 = \boxed{108}$$

The cross-out number is $\boxed{}$.

CROSS OUT SOMETHING

GA1433

Cross Out Something

C. The sum of the numbers in this series is ☐175☐ .

$8 + 17 + 19 + 23 + 32 + 35 + 41 = $ ☐175☐

Cross out one number so that the sum will be ☐152☐ .

$8 + 17 + 19 + 23 + 32 + 35 + 41 = $ ☐152☐

The cross-out number is ☐ .

D. The sum of the numbers in this series is ☐323☐.

$22 + 34 + 37 + 45 + 53 + 62 + 70 = $ ☐323☐

Cross out two numbers so that the sum will be ☐231☐ .

$22 + 34 + 37 + 45 + 53 + 62 + 70 = $ ☐231☐

The cross-out numbers are ☐ , ☐ .

GA1433

Cross Out Something

E. The sum of the numbers in this series is 209 .

$$31 + 38 + 32 + 37 + 35 + 36 = 209$$

Cross out two numbers so that the sum will be 142 .

The cross-out numbers are ☐ , ☐ .

F. The sum of the numbers in this series is 223 .

$$26 + 38 + 25 + 43 + 52 + 39 = 223$$

Cross out two numbers so that the sum will be 132 .

The cross-out numbers are ☐ , ☐ .

Share with the other groups the strategy used by your group in arriving at answers to the questions.

GA1433

This Is Really, Really Odd!

SKILLS: Odd-Even Numbers
Basic Skill Facts
Patterning

The objective of this really, really odd task is for your group to write numbers in each column so that the sum of the four digits is not an even number. The columns in the grid are identified by the letters **A**, **B**, **C** and **D**.

Here are additional rules that will help you and your group to successfully complete this activity.

Numbers placed in a row may not be repeated.

A	B	C	D		Sum
5	6	6	4	=	21

This error shows two columns (B and C) with the same digit.

Once numbers are placed in a column, they may not be repeated.

A	B	C	D		Sum
5	4	1	3	=	13
1	4	5	7	=	17

This time the error lies in column B.

B
4
4

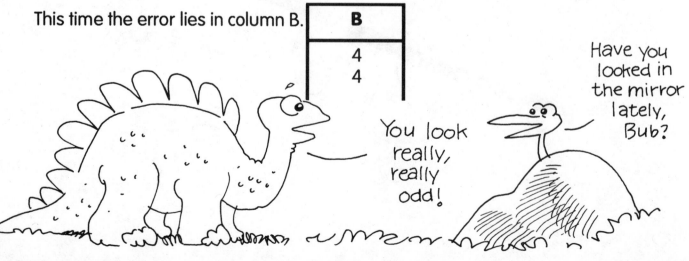

You look really, really odd!

Have you looked in the mirror lately, Bub?

10

GA1433

This Is Really, Really Odd!

Final rule . . . only the numerals 0 through 9 may be used.

A	B	C	D		Sum
5	7	4	15	=	31

The error that disqualifies this answer is the use of the number 15 in column D.

GA1433

This Is Really, Really Odd!

Complete this grid. Follow these rules.
1. The sum of the four numerals must be odd.
2. The numerals in each row may not be repeated.
3. The numerals in each column may not be repeated.
4. You may use only the numerals 0 to 9.

Be ready to share your findings with other groups at the end of this activity.

	A	B	C	D		Sum
1.						
2.						
3.						
4.						
5.						
6.						
7.						
8.						
9.						
10.						

GA1433

This Is the Challenge!
These Are the Facts

SKILLS: Problem Solving
Logic
Basic Skill Facts

I'm Sally!   I'm Sam!   I'm Sue!   I'm Serena!

I'm Sonny... and we're all friends!

If Sam is . . . then Sue must be . . . .

This is the challenge! Given the information below and then following a brief discussion period, can your group of experts determine as well as agree upon the ages of the following?

The Facts

Sally, Sam, Sue, Serena and Sonny are friends.
Sally is 6 years younger than Sam and 6 years older than Serena.
Serena is twice as old as Sue.
Sonny is half the age of Sam.
Sam, the oldest of the five people, is 18 years old.

The Findings

Sally	is [ ] years old.
Sam	is [ ] years old.
Sue	is [ ] years old.
Serena	is [ ] years old.
Sonny	is [ ] years old.

Clue: The total in years for all of the friends is 48 years.

This Is the Challenge!
These Are the Facts

Alan, Michele, Mark, Dawn and Robyn are all fifth graders who share many things in common. One of the things that they enjoy most of all is reading books for fun.

The Facts

Mark read 7 books more than Robyn.
Robyn read 4 books more than Dawn.
Dawn read half as many books as Michele.
Michele read 3 books more than Alan.
Alan read 9 books.

My mind's made up! Don't confuse me with facts!

The Findings

Mark	read ☐ books.
Robyn	read ☐ books.
Dawn	read ☐ books.
Michele	read ☐ books.
Alan	read ☐ books.

Clue: The five classmates read a combined sum of 54 books.

GA1433

This Is the Challenge!
These Are the Facts

The New Jersey State Aquarium decided to fill a large tank with the following fish: sharks, sea bass, flounder, fluke and stingrays. What are the exact amounts of each fish in the tank?

The Facts

There are twice as many sharks as stingrays.
There are four times the amount of flounder as there are sharks.
The amount of sea bass is half the number of flounder.
There are 6 more fluke than flounder.
The tank has 23 stingrays.

The Findings

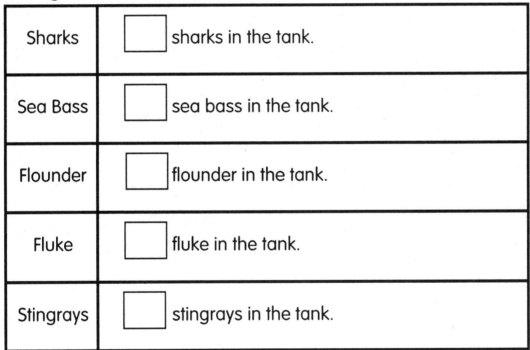

Sharks	☐ sharks in the tank.
Sea Bass	☐ sea bass in the tank.
Flounder	☐ flounder in the tank.
Fluke	☐ fluke in the tank.
Stingrays	☐ stingrays in the tank.

Clue: There is a total of 535 fish in the tank.

This Is the Challenge!
These Are the Facts

Dana and her friend Scott are neighbors who reside next door to each other. They live in a very small town. The town has one Main Street. This street is crowded with forty shops. These shops fall into six categories: shoe stores, clothing stores, electronic centers, bookstores, toy stores and restaurants.

The Facts

There are 8 more restaurants than toy stores.
The toy stores number half the number of shoe stores.
The number of clothing stores are twice the number of shoe stores.
The number of electronic centers and bookstores are each one third the number of clothing stores.
There are 3 toy stores.

The Findings

Toy Stores	☐ toy stores on Main Street.
Restaurants	☐ restaurants on Main Street.
Shoe Stores	☐ shoe stores on Main Street.
Clothing Stores	☐ clothing stores on Main Street.
Electronic Centers	☐ electronic centers on Main Street.
Book-stores	☐ bookstores on Main Street.

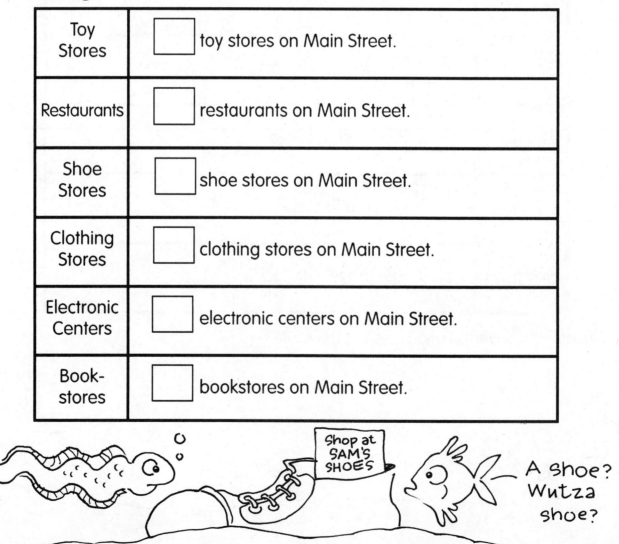

Shop at SAM'S SHOES

A shoe? Wutza shoe?

GA1433

This Is the Challenge!
These Are the Facts

Todd, Theresa, Terrence, Timmy and Tyler are baseball card collectors. How many cards does each collector own?

The Facts

Todd has 3 times the collection of Timmy.
Timmy's collection is half the size of Tyler's.
Tyler has 48 cards more than Terrence, who has 3 cards less than Theresa.
Theresa has 127 cards in her collection.

The Findings

Todd	has ☐ baseball cards.
Theresa	has ☐ baseball cards.
Terrence	has ☐ baseball cards.
Timmy	has ☐ baseball cards.
Tyler	has ☐ baseball cards.

Collectively this group has ☐ baseball cards.

GA1433

What Did You Say to Your Mom?

SKILLS: Problem Solving
Probability
Exponents

Suppose . . . just suppose that the following routine happened to you or to a member of your group. And suppose . . . just suppose that this routine happens to you every day for a month. Just as you get ready to leave your house and walk to school, your mom asks you a question.

The activity says that you may answer your mom with only a **yes** or **no**. You may never answer with a **maybe** because maybes are not allowed.

Every day, just as you are about to leave for school, your mom asks you one question more than the day before. On the second day of the month your mom asks you two questions. The question is on the second day, how many different ways could you have responded to your mom?

You could have said
  Yes, yes
  or
  No, no
  or
  Yes, no
  or
  No, yes . . . remember . . . no maybes.

So it is therefore quite possible that you may have responded to your mom in four different ways.

What did you say to your mom?

I told her, "I'm buzzin' off."

GA1433

What Did You Say to Your Mom?

Get together with your group members and record all of the possibilities as to different ways in which you may have responded to your mom's three questions on the third day.

3rd Day Responses

On the 3rd day I could have responded with ☐ responses.

4th Day Responses

On the 4th day I could have responded with ☐ responses.

5th Day Responses

On the 5th day I could have responded with ☐ responses.

GA1433

Names _____

Use the table to help you organize information gained through reading and pattern searching.

Day	Number of Responses
1	2
2	4
3	
4	
5	

Can your group determine the exact number of responses given by you on the 10th day of the month? 20th day of the month?

What did you say to your mom?

I told her, "Don't bug me."

20

A to Z

SKILLS: Place Value
Integration of Mathematics and Language Arts
Integration of Mathematics and Social Studies

The chart for this group activity is divided into four columns, and it is done alphabetically. The numerical value for each column is designated according to the concept of place value–ones, tens, hundreds and thousands. Below each numerical value is a specific set of letters.

Your team will be given a set of ten words. Each word is recorded on a separate 3" x 5" card. The team members are to alphabetize each word according to its initial letter. Once the correct column placement has been determined, one person in the group records that particular word in the designated column. At the completion of the recording of all ten words, team members should total the numerical value of the cards according to place value.

1000 A to G	100 H to N	10 O to T	1 U to Z
___	___	___	___
___	___	___	___
___	___	___	___
___	___	___	___
___	___	___	___
___	___	___	___
___	___	___	___
___	___	___	___
___	___	___	___
___	___	___	___

Example:
Suppose the following ten words were given to your group:

1. pencil
2. avenue
3. washer
4. special
5. decision
6. table
7. horse
8. dish
9. window
10. friend

A to Z

Your group would be asked to alphabetize each word according to its initial letter, and then record the word in its proper place value column. After all ten words are recorded, the group is to total its score according to place value.

1000 A to G	100 H to N	10 O to T	1 U to Z
avenue	horse	pencil	washer
decision		special	window
dish		table	
friend			

Scoring the ten words:

Four words are recorded in the thousands column = 4000
One word is recorded in the hundreds column   = 100
Three words are recorded in the tens column   =   30
Two words are recorded in the ones column   =   2
Score =   4132

22

A to Z

Try this practice set of cards with your group. Be sure to arrive at a score for the ten words.

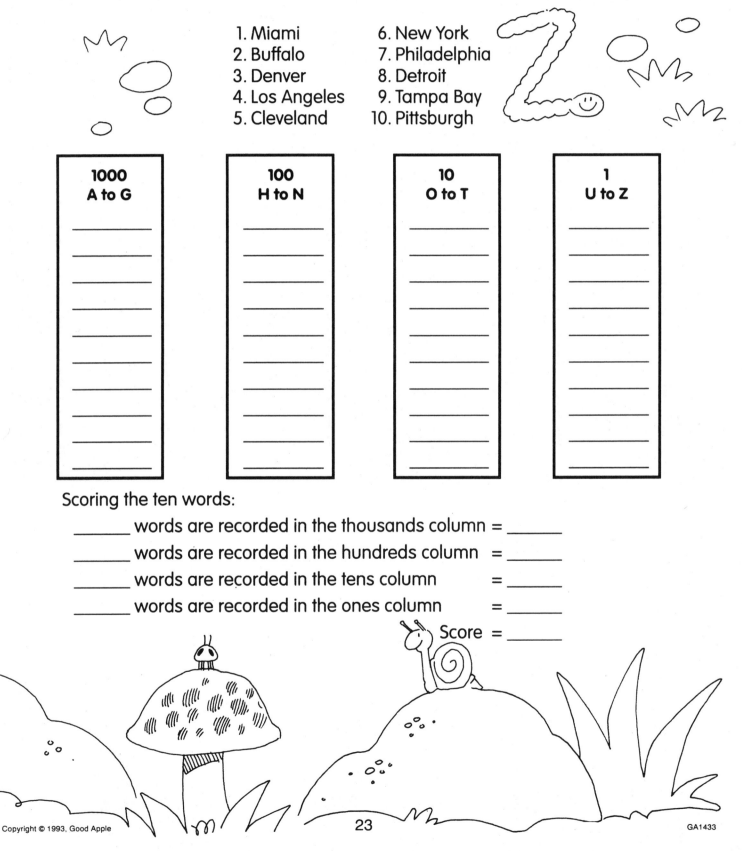

1. Miami
2. Buffalo
3. Denver
4. Los Angeles
5. Cleveland

6. New York
7. Philadelphia
8. Detroit
9. Tampa Bay
10. Pittsburgh

1000 A to G	100 H to N	10 O to T	1 U to Z
_____	_____	_____	_____
_____	_____	_____	_____
_____	_____	_____	_____
_____	_____	_____	_____
_____	_____	_____	_____
_____	_____	_____	_____
_____	_____	_____	_____
_____	_____	_____	_____
_____	_____	_____	_____
_____	_____	_____	_____

Scoring the ten words:

_____ words are recorded in the thousands column = _____

_____ words are recorded in the hundreds column = _____

_____ words are recorded in the tens column = _____

_____ words are recorded in the ones column = _____

Score = _____

GA1433

A to Z

Discuss this practice set of cards with your group. Be sure to arrive at a score for the ten words.

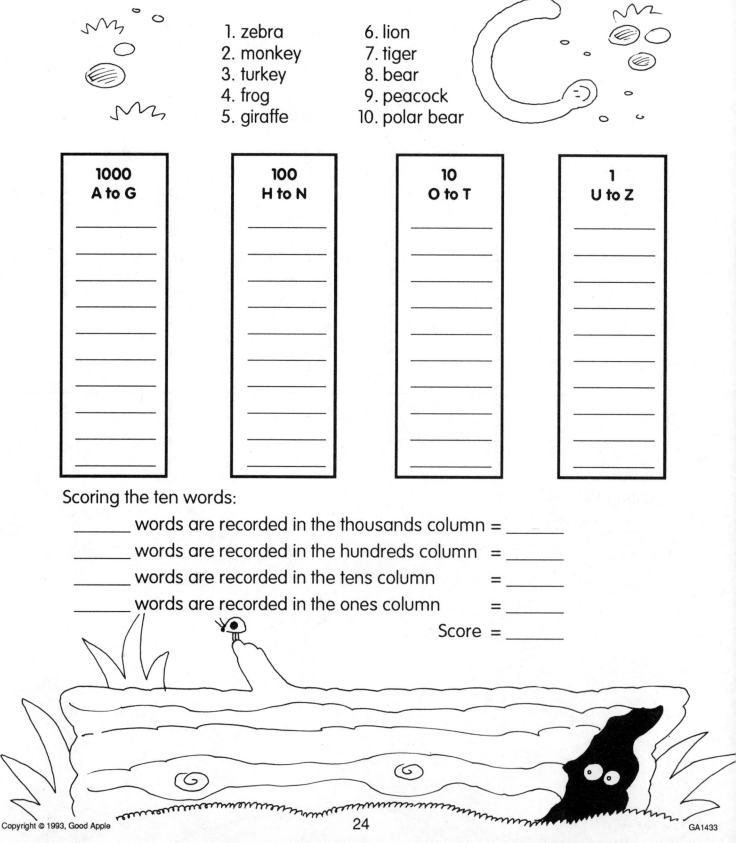

1. zebra
2. monkey
3. turkey
4. frog
5. giraffe

6. lion
7. tiger
8. bear
9. peacock
10. polar bear

1000 A to G	**100** H to N	**10** O to T	**1** U to Z
_____	_____	_____	_____
_____	_____	_____	_____
_____	_____	_____	_____
_____	_____	_____	_____
_____	_____	_____	_____
_____	_____	_____	_____
_____	_____	_____	_____
_____	_____	_____	_____
_____	_____	_____	_____
_____	_____	_____	_____

Scoring the ten words:

_____ words are recorded in the thousands column = _____

_____ words are recorded in the hundreds column = _____

_____ words are recorded in the tens column = _____

_____ words are recorded in the ones column = _____

Score = _____

GA1433

Names _____

A to Z

Record the ten words given to your group.

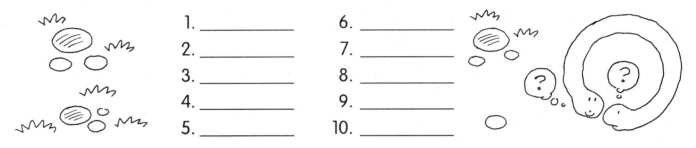

1. _____   6. _____
2. _____   7. _____
3. _____   8. _____
4. _____   9. _____
5. _____   10. _____

Alphabetize each word and record it in the proper place value column.

1000 A to G	100 H to N	10 O to T	1 U to Z
_____	_____	_____	_____
_____	_____	_____	_____
_____	_____	_____	_____
_____	_____	_____	_____
_____	_____	_____	_____
_____	_____	_____	_____
_____	_____	_____	_____
_____	_____	_____	_____
_____	_____	_____	_____
_____	_____	_____	_____

Scoring the ten words:

_____ words are recorded in the thousands column = _____

_____ words are recorded in the hundreds column = _____

_____ words are recorded in the tens column   = _____

_____ words are recorded in the ones column   = _____

Score = _____

GA1433

Making "Pals"

SKILLS: Column Addition with Regrouping
Palindromes
Problem Solving

How many steps are necessary in order to create a palindromic number?
413 is not a palindromic number. However if you were to reverse the order of
these digits and then use addition . . . a palindrome!

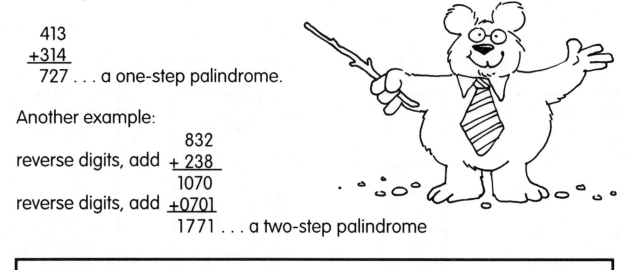

```
  413
 +314
  727 . . . a one-step palindrome.
```

Another example:

```
                         832
reverse digits, add   + 238
                        1070
reverse digits, add   +0701
                        1771 . . . a two-step palindrome
```

Try this problem.
327–How many steps are necessary to create a palindromic number?

Making "Pals"

Each of the problems on this sheet begins with numbers that are not palindromes. Your group is charged with two things.

How many steps are necessary to reach the palindrome? What is the palindromic number?

A.
419

Take ☐ steps.

The palindrome is ☐ .

B.
846

Take ☐ steps.

The palindrome is ☐ .

C.
574

Take ☐ steps.

The palindrome is ☐ .

D.
275

Take ☐ steps.

The palindrome is ☐ .

*Your group might want to use a calculator for this work sheet.

GA1433

Making "Pals"

Each of the problems on this sheet begins with numbers that are not palindromes. Your group is charged with two things.

How many steps are necessary to reach the palindrome? What is the palindromic number?

E.

392

Take ☐ steps.

The palindrome is ☐ .

F.

349

Take ☐ steps.

The palindrome is ☐ .

G.

886

Take ☐ steps.

The palindrome is ☐ .

H.

Can your group find a three-digit number that will require more than eight steps to reach a palindrome?

---

*Your group might want to use a calculator for this work sheet.

GA1433

Which "Pal" Is Closest?

SKILLS: Palindromes
Addition, Subtraction with and Without Regrouping
Problem Solving

A palindromic number is one that may be read backward or forward.
535; 8228; 26,462

The following are examples of numbers that are not palindromes:
438; 735; 1484; 64,757

The following are examples of numbers that are palindromes:
434; 737; 1441; 64,746

This activity will deal with creating three-digit palindromic numbers.

To accomplish this, your group will use the operations of addition and subtraction. Start with a nonpalindromic number such as 482. This will be known as the start number. Once the start number has been determined, the group must decide on the closest palindrome greater than the start number and the closest palindrome less than the start number.

Consider the example with the start number 482.

The closest palindrome greater than 482 is 484.
The closest palindrome less than 482 is 474.

To reach 484, your group would have to add 2 to 482.
482 + 2 = 484

To reach 474, your group would have to subtract 8 from 482.
482 - 8 = 474

HIYa, PaL!

GA1433

Which "Pal" Is Closest?

Therefore the closest palindrome (or "pal") to 482 can be reached through addition.

Another example:
  The start number is . . . 278
  The closest palindrome greater than 278 is . . . 282
  The closest palindrome less than 278 is . . . 272

Addition	Subtraction
start number 278 + 4 closest palindrome 282	start number 278 - 6 closest palindrome 272

The closest palindrome to the start number 278 is 282.

Reason: 282 is four numbers from 278; whereas, 272 is six numbers from 278.

GA1433

Which "Pal" Is Closest?

Remember, your group must first find the closest palindrome for addition and then the closest palindrome for subtraction.

A.

Addition	**Subtraction**
start number 581	start number 581
+ ☐	– ☐
closest palindrome ☐	closest palindrome ☐

The closest "pal" to 581 is ☐ .

B.

Addition	**Subtraction**
start number 871	start number 871
+ ☐	– ☐
closest palindrome ☐	closest palindrome ☐

The closest "pal" to 871 is ☐ .

C.

Addition	**Subtraction**
start number 249	start number 249
+ ☐	– ☐
closest palindrome ☐	closest palindrome ☐

The closest "pal" to 249 is ☐ .

D.

Addition	**Subtraction**
start number 308	start number 308
+ ☐	– ☐
closest palindrome ☐	closest palindrome ☐

The closest "pal" to 308 is ☐ .

HIYA, PAL!

Even Steven

SKILLS: Multiplication
Factors
Problem Solving

Another problem for your group to consider: When trying to reach as many possible solutions as you can, it is most important that all of the group members discuss and share as many avenues as possible that might be used to reach this goal.

The Problem

Working together, your group has created a brand-new card game and the entire deck of this brand-new card game is comprised of 24 cards.

The main rule with regard to this game is that all of the cards in the deck must be EVENLY DISTRIBUTED among all of the players in the game. There CANNOT BE ANY CARDS LEFT OVER.

It is up to your group to determine how many players may participate in this new card game.

Even Steven

In this table, list all of the possible solutions if the deck of cards numbered 24.

Example:
1. The 24 cards can be evenly dealt to 24 players. Each player would receive 1 card.
2. The 24 cards can be evenly dealt to 1 player. This player would receive 24 cards.

Complete this table.

Even Steven: 24 cards

Number of Players	Number of Cards for Each Player
24	1
1	24

GA1433

Even Steven

Complete this table.

Even Steven: 36 cards

Number of Players		Number of Cards for Each Player

Complete this table.

Even Steven: 52 cards

Number of Players		Number of Cards for Each Player

34

GA1433

Even Steven

Complete this table.

Even Steven: 56 cards

Number of Players	Number of Cards for Each Player

Complete this table.

Even Steven: 100 cards

Number of Players	Number of Cards for Each Player

GA1433

Identification Problems

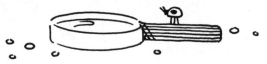

SKILLS: Problem Solving
        Patterning

You and the members of your group have a fine reputation as being top-notch problem solvers. For this reason your group has been chosen to solve something that is known as "identification problems." Possible methods for arriving at solutions can be found in examples A and B.

Each problem will refer to a specific number of coins that are to be considered at the problem's outset. The second clue toward reaching a solution is the "trade in" value of the total coins. From all of the clues presented, your group is asked to determine the face value of each of the original coins.

Example A:
   This problem is about seven coins. The coins that make up this group are nickels and pennies. If you were to trade in all of the seven coins for pennies, you would have a total of fifteen pennies.

Question:
   What were the original coins? How many pennies and how many nickels?

   One method of arriving at a solution to this problem is to construct a pictorial representation of the original problem.

7 coins	◯ ◯ ◯ ◯ ◯ ◯ ◯	= 15 pennies
1 penny, 6 nickels	① ⑤ ⑤ ⑤ ⑤ ⑤ ⑤	= 31 pennies
2 pennies, 5 nickels	① ① ⑤ ⑤ ⑤ ⑤ ⑤	= 27 pennies
3 pennies, 4 nickels	① ① ① ⑤ ⑤ ⑤ ⑤	= 23 pennies
4 pennies, 3 nickels	① ① ① ① ⑤ ⑤ ⑤	= 19 pennies
5 pennies, 2 nickels	① ① ① ① ① ⑤ ⑤	= 15 pennies . . . the solution

Identification Problems

Another approach to solving example A.

Construct the following table:

Pennies	Nickels		Total
0	7	=	35 pennies
1	6	=	31 pennies
2	5	=	27 pennies
3	4	=	23 pennies
4	3	=	19 pennies
5	2	=	15 pennies . . . the solution

Example B:

This problem is about four coins. The coins that make up the group are nickels and dimes. If you were able to trade in the four coins for pennies, there would be a total of thirty-five pennies.

Question: What were the original coins?

Nickels	Dimes		Total
0	4	=	40 pennies
1	3	=	35 pennies . . . the solution

Represented here are but two of the many creative methods that are open to your imagination.

GA1433

Identification Problems

A.

This problem is about five coins. The coins are pennies and dimes. If you were to trade in all five coins for pennies, you would have twenty-three pennies.

Question: What were the original coins? How many pennies; how many dimes?

B.

This problem is about six coins. The coins are nickels and quarters. If you were to trade in all six coins for pennies, you would have seventy pennies.

Question: What were the original coins? How many nickels; how many quarters?

I'm with the census bureau!

GA1433

Identification Problems

C.

This problem is about ten coins. The coins are pennies and quarters. If you were to trade in all ten coins for pennies, you would have eighty-two pennies.

Question: What were the original coins? How many pennies; how many quarters?

D.

This problem is about eight coins. The coins are dimes and quarters. If you were to trade in all eight coins for pennies, you would have one hundred ten pennies.

Question: What were the original coins? How many dimes; how many quarters?

Identification Problems

E.

This problem is about six coins. The coins are dimes and quarters. If you were to trade in all six coins for nickels, you would have twenty-one nickels.

Question: What were the original coins? How many dimes; how many quarters?

F.

This problem is about seven coins. The coins are dimes and quarters. If you were to trade in all seven coins for nickels, you would have thirty-two nickels.

Question: What were the original coins? How many dimes; how many quarters.

I'm with the census bureau. Anybody home?

40

Alpha Values

SKILLS: Problem Solving
Integration of Mathematics and Language Arts
Basic Facts

A	B	C	D	E	F	G	H	I	J	K	L	M
1	2	3	4	5	6	7	8	9	10	11	12	13

N	O	P	Q	R	S	T	U	V	W	X	Y	Z
14	15	16	17	18	19	20	21	22	23	24	25	26

The class forms groups with three to five members. Each group is to find the point value of ten words. All of the words should have a point value from 50 inclusive to 59 points.

For example, a fourth grade group consisting of three girls and two boys discovered ten words with a point value range of 50 to 59.

F O R K
6 + 15 + 18 + 11 = 50

W I N E
23 + 9 + 14 + 5 = 51

D O O R
4 + 15 + 15 + 18 = 52

M A S T
13 + 1 + 19 + 20 = 53

P O R E
16 + 15 + 18 + 5 = 54

C H E S T
3 + 8 + 5 + 19 + 20 = 55

T I R E D
20 + 9 + 18 + 5 + 4 = 56

S H A R K
19 + 8 + 1 + 18 + 11 = 57

G L A S S
7 + 12 + 1 + 19 + 19 = 58

W I S H
23 + 9 + 19 + 8 = 59

GA1433

Alpha Values

A	B	C	D	E	F	G	H	I	J	K	L	M
1	2	3	4	5	6	7	8	9	10	11	12	13

N	O	P	Q	R	S	T	U	V	W	X	Y	Z
14	15	16	17	18	19	20	21	22	23	24	25	26

Team Members

_____

_____

_____

_____

Find a word for each of the following point values.

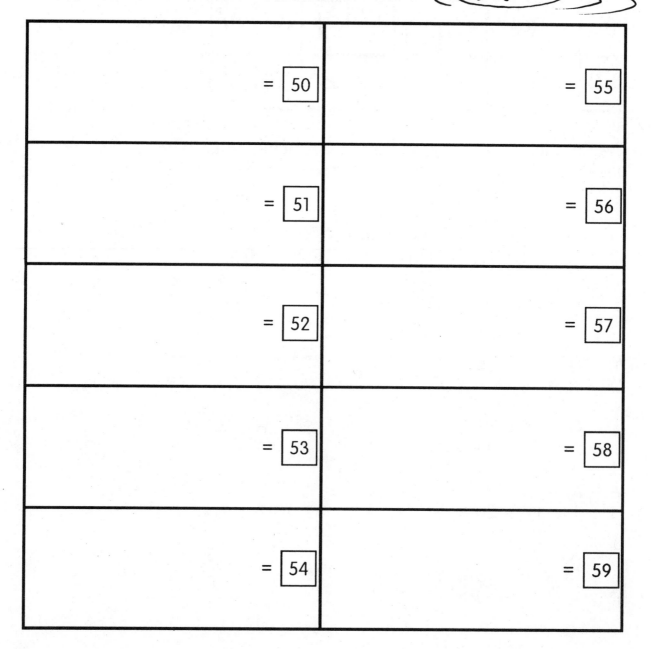

= 50	= 55
= 51	= 56
= 52	= 57
= 53	= 58
= 54	= 59

GA1433

Alpha Values

A	B	C	D	E	F	G	H	I	J	K	L	M
1	2	3	4	5	6	7	8	9	10	11	12	13

Team Members

_____

_____

_____

_____

_____

_____

N	O	P	Q	R	S	T	U	V	W	X	Y	Z
14	15	16	17	18	19	20	21	22	23	24	25	26

Set your own point values.

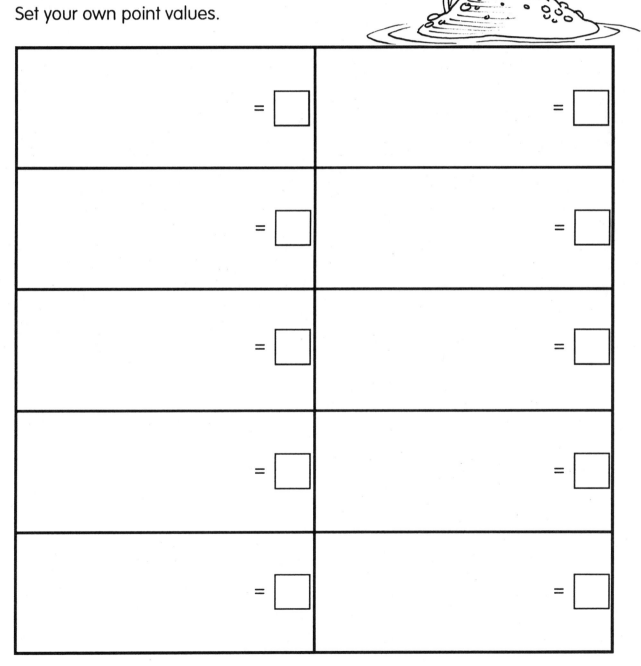

GA1433

Match Me!

SKILLS: Problem Solving
        Patterning
        Basic Facts

Arrange the class into four groups. Allow each group the opportunity to select a color name from the following:

yellow, red, white, blue

Once color names have been decided, it becomes the objective of each group to find the match for each color word, or another way of saying this . . . **each group is to decide upon the specific match for all four colors.** Group members should ready themselves so that they will be able to reason through as well as be able to explain their choices.

For example:

Color Words	Match Words
1. yellow	1. room
2. red	2. window
3. white	3. blackboard
4. blue	4. yard

Presented to all four color groups at the chalkboard.

Cooperatively, each group will now decide on the four color and word matches.

Any of the groups might say, "Our choices are yellow to yard, red to room, white to window, blue to blackboard, and our reasoning is, we are matching the initial letter of the color word with the initial letter of the match word."

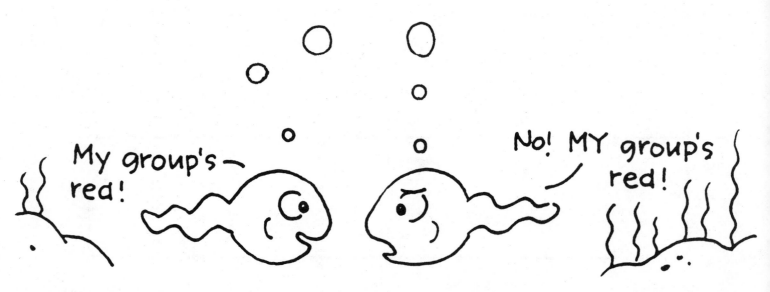

44

Match Me!

Another example:

Again, at the chalkboard . . . .

Color Words	Match Words
1. yellow	1. sky
2. red	2. snow
3. white	3. banana
4. blue	4. blood

The Blue group might say, "Our choices are yellow to banana, red to blood, white to snow, blue to sky, and our reasoning is, we have chosen to match the color words with the particular colors that come to mind when you associate both. (color and match . . . white with snow)

The teacher can write the color words and match words on the chalkboard and give each group about five minutes to arrive at their own determinations.

Groups will then share their responses with the entire class.

GA1433

Match Me!

Another example:

Color Words	Match Words
1. yellow	1. _____
2. red	2. _____
3. white	3. _____
4. blue	4. _____

You can't match me...I'm matchless!

Our choice of matches. We are the _____ team.

Another example:

Color Words		Match Words
1. yellow	to	1. _____
2. red	to	2. _____
3. white	to	3. _____
4. blue	to	4. _____

Our reasons for our choices:

_____
_____
_____
_____
_____
_____
_____
_____

GA1433

Match Me!

A.	yellow	blocks
	red	whiskers
	white	yum yums
	blue	roses

F.	yellow	51
	red	61
	white	41
	blue	31

B.	yellow	wren
	red	yak
	white	bear
	blue	rooster

G.	yellow	18
	red	12
	white	9
	blue	15

C.	yellow	apple
	red	milk
	white	banana
	blue	berry

H.	yellow	three
	red	four
	white	six
	blue	five

D.	yellow	Ryan
	red	Yolanda
	white	William
	blue	Barbara

I.	yellow	16
	red	36
	white	25
	blue	9

E.	yellow	fish
	red	rabbit
	white	yak
	blue	moose

J.	yellow	140
	red	2130
	white	7160
	blue	50

Play Match Me? Why not? I don't have a heavy schedule today.

GA1433

Column A or Column B?

SKILLS: Problem Solving
           Patterning
           Attributes

Your group is asked to carefully examine the following numbers:

1	2	3	4	5	6	7	8	9	10
11	12	13	14	15	16	17	18	19	20

All of the problems for your group's consideration will be arranged into three parts headed by **Column A, Column B, Common Attribute for All of the Numbers in Column A.**

Your job is to decide what exactly ties all of the numbers in **Column A** together. What specific attribute do all of these numbers possess? All of the members of **Column B** are void of this particular attribute.

Examples:

Column A	Column B	Common Attribute for All of the Numbers in Column A
(1) 1, 3, 5, 7, 9, 11, 13, 15, 17, 19	2, 4, 6, 8, 10, 12, 14, 16, 18, 20	All Column A numbers are odd.
(2) 1, 2, 3, 4, 5, 6, 7, 8, 9	11, 12, 13, 14, 15, 16, 17, 18, 19, 20	All Column A numbers are less than 10.
(3) 5, 10, 15, 20	1, 2, 3, 4, 6, 7, 8, 9, 11, 12, 13, 14, 16, 17, 18, 19	All Column A numbers are multiples of 5.

Column A or Column B?

1	2	3	4	5	6	7	8	9	10
11	12	13	14	15	16	17	18	19	20

Column A	Column B	Common Attribute for All of the Numbers in Column A
(1) 1, 4, 9, 16	2, 3, 5, 6, 7, 8, 10, 11, 12, 13, 14, 15, 17, 18, 19, 20	
(2) 1, 4, 7, 11, 14, 17	2, 3, 5, 6, 8, 9, 10, 12, 13, 15, 16, 18, 19, 20	
(3) 2, 12, 20	1, 3, 4, 5, 6, 7, 8, 9, 10, 11, 13, 14, 15, 16, 17, 18, 19	
(4) 6, 7, 17	1, 2, 3, 4, 5, 8, 9, 10, 11, 12, 13, 14, 15, 16, 18, 19, 20	

Column A or Column B?

1	2	3	4	5	6	7	8	9	10
11	12	13	14	15	16	17	18	19	20

Column A	Column B	Common Attribute for All of the Numbers in Column A
(1) 1, 2, 6, 10	3, 4, 5, 7, 8, 9, 11, 12, 13, 14, 15, 16, 17, 18, 19, 20	
(2) 1, 2, 4, 8	3, 5, 6, 7, 9, 10 11, 12, 13, 14, 15, 16, 17, 18, 19, 20	
(3) 7, 13, 14, 15, 16, 18, 19, 20	1, 2, 3, 4, 5, 6, 8, 9, 10, 11, 12, 17	
(4) 2, 3, 5, 7, 11, 13, 17, 19	1, 4, 6, 8, 9, 10, 12, 14, 15, 16, 18, 20	

Can You Prove It?

— My addends have been missing for YEARS!

The two shapes in the example below are a circle and a triangle. In addition to the shapes, you are also given a numeral assigned to each shape. The example indicates that the sum of both numerals or the value of both shapes combined is 6. Your job and that of your group is to decide on the value of each shape and to record your reasons.

Example:
A.

⬤	+	△	= 6

Possible Solutions:

	⬤		△	
1.	0	+	6	= 6
2.	1	+	5	= 6
3.	2	+	4	= 6
4.	4	+	2	= 6
5.	5	+	1	= 6
6.	6	+	0	= 6

Any of these equations are possible answers to the problem. One answer that is not acceptable is 3 + 3 = 6. The reason is that the two given shapes (circle and triangle) are not alike and therefore the addends in the equation must be different.

51

GA1433

Can You Prove It?

Another example:
This problem involves three shapes and three addends. The sum of the addends is 8.

Looks like another one of those SHAPE GAMES.

B.

○	+	△	+	▯	= 8

Possible Solutions:

	○	+	△	+	▯	
1.	5	+	2	+	1	= 8
2.	5	+	3	+	0	= 8
3.	3	+	4	+	1	= 8
4.	0	+	2	+	6	= 8

And still another example:
This problem involves three steps and three addends. The sum of the addends is 10.

△	+	○	+	◯	= 10

Possible Solutions:

	△	+	○	+	◯	
1.	6	+	2	+	2	= 10
2.	0	+	5	+	5	= 10
3.	2	+	4	+	4	= 10
4.	8	+	1	+	1	= 10

Each group is to record as many equations as possible. All of the equations recorded should fit the shapes as well as the sum of the individual problem. Each problem will be given a designated time limit. The group with the most correct responses will be determined the winner.

Can You Prove It?

The following problem has a five-minute time limit.
Three shapes and the sum is 9.

Possible
Solutions:

□	+	▯	+	◯	= 9
1.					
2.					
3.					
4.					
5.					
6.					
7.					
8.					
9.					
10.					
11.					
12.					
13.					
14.					
15.					

That looks
easy enough,
and, hey, I'm
not heavily
booked...

GA1433

Names _____

Can You Prove It?

The following problem has a five-minute time limit.
Three shapes and the sum is 12.

Possible
Solutions:

I toldja!
Another one
of those
SHAPE
GAMES.

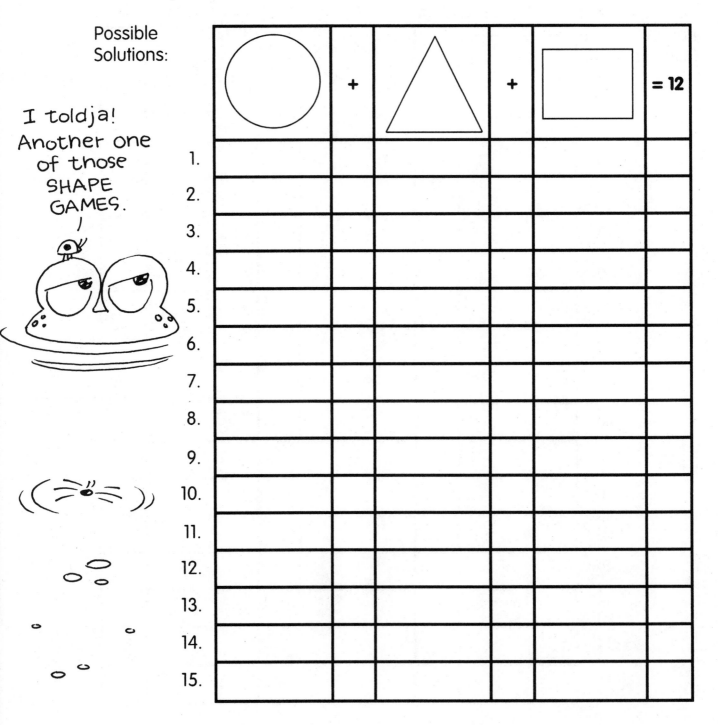

⭘	+	△	+	▢	= 12
1.					
2.					
3.					
4.					
5.					
6.					
7.					
8.					
9.					
10.					
11.					
12.					
13.					
14.					
15.					

Names_____

Can You Prove It?

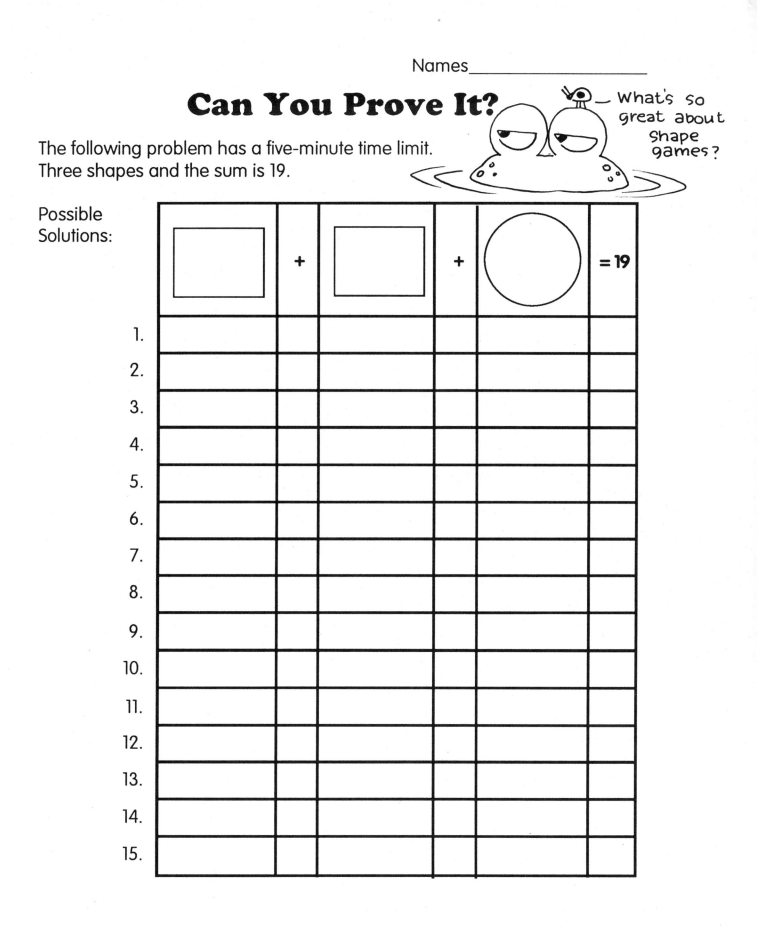

what's so great about shape games?

The following problem has a five-minute time limit. Three shapes and the sum is 19.

Possible Solutions:

	□	+	□	+	○	= 19
1.						
2.						
3.						
4.						
5.						
6.						
7.						
8.						
9.						
10.						
11.						
12.						
13.						
14.						
15.						

GA1433

Can You Prove It?

The following problem has a ten-minute time limit.
Three shapes and the sum is 26.

Possible
Solutions:

⬤	+	△	+	▯	= 26
1.					
2.					
3.					
4.					
5.					
6.					
7.					
8.					
9.					
10.					
11.					
12.					
13.					
14.					
15.					
16.					
17.					
18.					
19.					
20.					

They keep your
brain in shape!

GA1433

Add On!

SKILLS: Problem Solving
       Reading
       Writing
       Language Arts

This is a round-robin type of activity. Arrange the class into three, four or five groups. Each group will have the responsibility of writing one sentence of a three-sentence word problem.

Suppose Group A wrote the following:

> There were twenty-six players on the Panthers Little League baseball team.

Each of the other groups writes the first line of their word problem in much the same order. All of the groups will now exchange papers being sure not to get back their original problem.

Once Group A receives another group's paper with the first sentence of a word problem, Group A will write their version of the second sentence. In the meantime the group that has Group A's first sentence will add to it their own second sentence.

Eight of the players are girls.

This group will pass the two sentences on to any other group but Group A. It is the responsibility of the third group to write the problem's final sentence and provide the answer.

> How many of the players were boys? (18 boys)

Want to play Add On?

I'm too slow for round robin games.

Add On!

To make group identification of the sentences easier, offer each group, a different color crayon to write their part of the word problem.

Another example using three groups:

Group A: A very large hotel offered 125 rooms to guests.

Group B: At the end of the first day, there were no vacancies at the hotel and the number of guests staying at the hotel totaled 375.

Group C: What was the average number of hotel guests staying in each room?

GA1433

Names _____

Add On!

Group A: Sentence 1

Group B: Sentence 2

Group C: Sentence 3

Answer _____

Final Goal

SKILLS: Problem Solving
       Addition
       Missing Addends

Arrange the class into groups of four to five students. Assign each group the task of coming up with their own group name. The cooperative learning experience will begin with the teacher reading the names of the groups and announcing that each group will begin play at an initial start number and end play at a final or goal number.

For example:
Suppose the start number is 9 and the goal number is 50. The teacher will continue the instructions by saying that it is the job of each team to select five addends from the numbers 1 through 12. Each addend chosen is to be added to the previous sum, remembering that each group's objective is to arrive at the final goal. In this instance the final goal is 50.

The teacher will then announce the first lead team and ask that all of the teams begin with the sum of 9, use five additional addends and end with a final goal of 50. All of the teams should keep their selections (choice of addends) secret and reveal them only when asked by the designated lead team.

When all of the teams have announced that they have reached the final goal of 50, the teacher will instruct the lead team to disclose their five steps, one at a time. As the lead team uncovers each step, they will earn five points each time that their sum is matched by another team.

what's your group name? — "Slug Fest."

GA1433

Final Goal

Lead Team

Step 1: lead team announces 9 + 5 = 14
The lead team earns five points from all other teams that have reached the sum of 14.

Step 2: lead team announces 14 + 11 = 25
Again, five points for the lead team for every other team with the sum of 25.

Step 3: lead team announces 25 + 6 = 31

Step 4: lead team announces 31 + 12 = 43

Step 5: lead team announces 43 + 7 = 50

*There is no scoring on the fifth step since all of the teams will reach the final goal.

Play begins anew with each of the other teams having a chance to be designated as the lead team.

Players who are not members of the lead team have as their objective the challenge of selecting an addend that will allow them to reach an unlikely sum. For example, for the sum of 33, select the addend 6 as opposed to the addend 7.   33 + 6 = 39
33 + 7 = 40

This cooperative activity can be used with any initial number and any final goal.

GA1433

Final Goal

Variations to the activity might be to combine operations as opposed to only using the addition operation.

Example:

"Today the operations of choice are addition and multiplication."

Suppose the lead team might want to advance its sum by 12.

When asked to reveal their scoring procedure, they might have responded with

$$9 + 12 = 21 \ldots \text{we used addition}$$
$$\text{or}$$
$$9 + (4 \times 3) = 21 \ldots \text{we used multiplication}$$

However, for the lead team to score points, other teams must not only be at 21 but must also use the same operation.

Sorry, kids...
slim pickin's today...

GA1433

Final Goal

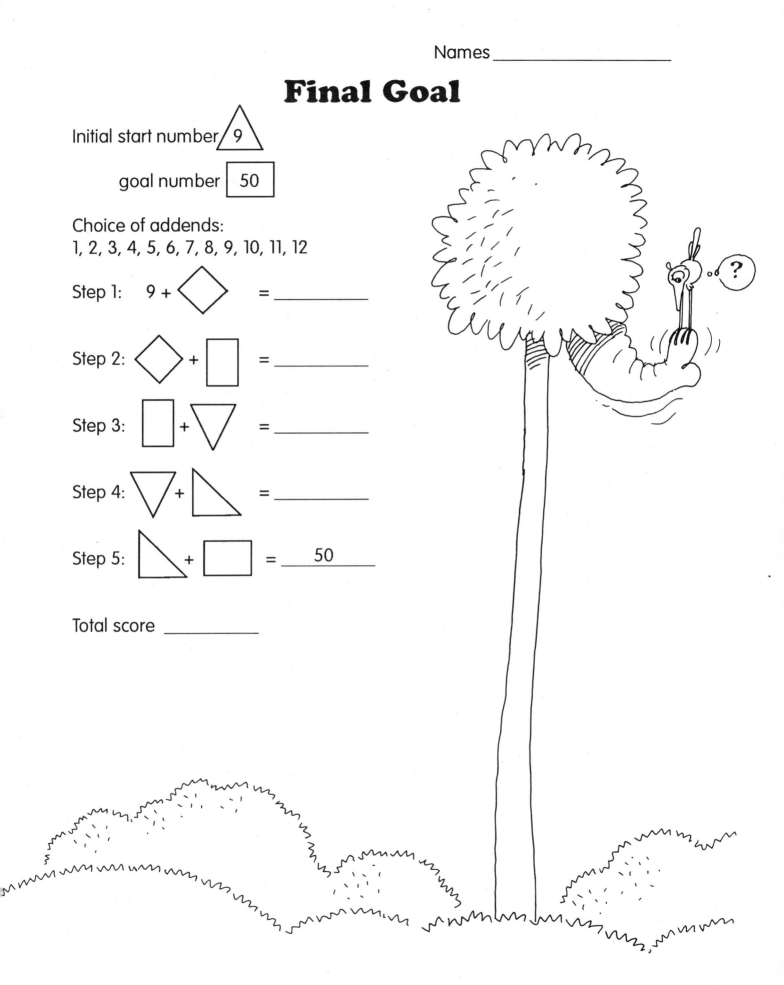

Initial start number △ 9

goal number ☐ 50

Choice of addends:
1, 2, 3, 4, 5, 6, 7, 8, 9, 10, 11, 12

Step 1:   9 + ◇   = _____

Step 2:   ◇ + ☐   = _____

Step 3:   ☐ + ▽   = _____

Step 4:   ▽ + ◿   = _____

Step 5:   ◺ + ☐   = ___50___

Total score _____

GA1433

Our Destination Is . . .

SKILLS: Problem Solving
Estimation
Integration of Mathematics
Integration of Social Studies

This activity is for two to five groups. Each of the groups will need a map of the United States.

Allow each group approximately fifteen minutes to select a particular point of origin as well as a particular destination.

*All of the points of origin should have the same destination in mind and the object of this activity is to try to determine the destination before the four clues are given.

Example:
Suppose Group A chose   Boston, Mass.   as the secret destination. The group must then choose four different points of origin and give them one at a time.

Clue:
1. Our destination is 1300 miles from Miami, Florida.
2. Our destination is 550 miles from Cleveland, Ohio.
3. Our destination is 1250 miles from Denver, Colorado.
4. Our destination is 500 miles from Pittsburgh, Pennsylvania.

After each clue, allow the other groups one guess each at the mystery destination.

If the mystery destination was discovered after the first clue, Group A earns 4 points.
After the second clue, Group A earns 8 points.
After the third clue, Group A earns 12 points.
After the fourth clue, Group A earns 16 points.

If after all four clues are given and none of the other groups has discovered the mystery destination, then Group A will earn 30 points.

The activity continues with Group B following this same procedure.

Our Destination Is . . .

The teacher might wish to share additional examples with the class before having the groups work by themselves.

Secret Destination | Detroit, Michigan |

Clue 1: 650 miles from Philadelphia, Pennsylvania

Clue 2: 475 miles from St. Louis, Missouri

Clue 3: 1950 miles from Los Angeles, California

Clue 4: 1150 miles from Miami, Florida

Secret Destination | Cincinnati, Ohio |

Clue 1: 600 miles from New York City, New York

Clue 2: 700 miles from New Orleans, Louisiana

Clue 3: 2100 miles from San Francisco, California

Clue 4: 250 miles from Detroit, Michigan

Secret Destination | San Diego, California |

Clue 1: 1600 miles from New Orleans, Louisiana

Clue 2: 1150 miles from Seattle, Washington

Clue 3: 300 miles from Las Vegas, Nevada

Clue 4: 2300 miles from Baltimore, Maryland

NEW YORK CITY OR BUST!

"MAD MAX"

GA1433

Our Destination Is . . .

Our Secret Destination [   ]

Clue 1: [   ] miles from [   ]

Clue 2: [   ] miles from [   ]

Clue 3: [   ] miles from [   ]

Clue 4: [   ] miles from [   ]

Our score is [   ] points.

DETROIT OR BUST!

BEARLY AIRBORNE

GA1433

Sweater Time

SKILLS: Problem Solving
        Basic Facts

The following colors are assigned numerical values:

Red = 16
Blue = 8
Green = 4
Yellow = 2
White = 1

Now think of someone wearing an all-blue sweater. One student might say, "Gee, that's a really nice looking sweater." Since we know that certain colors have been assigned certain values, we would know that this "really nice looking blue sweater" has a numerical value of 8. We also know that a sweater with the colors blue and yellow has a numerical value of 8 + 2 = 10.

Another example might be to determine the numerical value of a sweater with the colors red, yellow and white.

Red = 16, Yellow = 2, White = 1 = 16 + 2 + 1 = 19
The sweater has a numerical value of 19.

Working cooperatively in your small groups, find the numerical value of the colorful sweaters.

GA1433

Sweater Time

It is the responsibility of each group to determine the numerical value of each sweater.

Arrive at your answer by using addition only.

Answers are determined by color. It doesn't matter how many times a particular color is seen in a sweater.

Red = 16   Blue = 8   Green = 4   Yellow = 2   White = 1

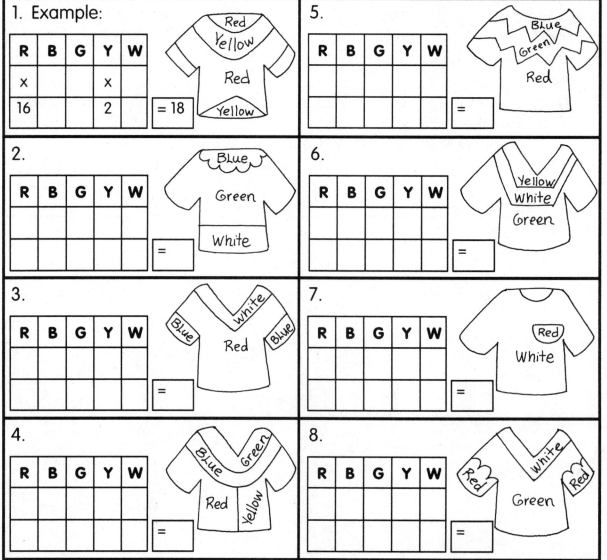

1. Example:

R	B	G	Y	W
x			x	
16			2	

= 18

Red
Yellow

Red

Yellow

5.

R	B	G	Y	W

=

Blue
Green

Red

2.

R	B	G	Y	W

=

Blue

Green

White

6.

R	B	G	Y	W

=

Yellow
White
Green

3.

R	B	G	Y	W

=

Blue   White   Blue

Red

7.

R	B	G	Y	W

=

Red
White

4.

R	B	G	Y	W

=

Blue   Green

Red   Yellow

8.

R	B	G	Y	W

=

White
Red   Green   Red

GA1433

Sweater Time

Can your group determine the colors that make up each of the following sweaters?

Red = 16   Blue = 8   Green = 4   Yellow = 2   White = 1

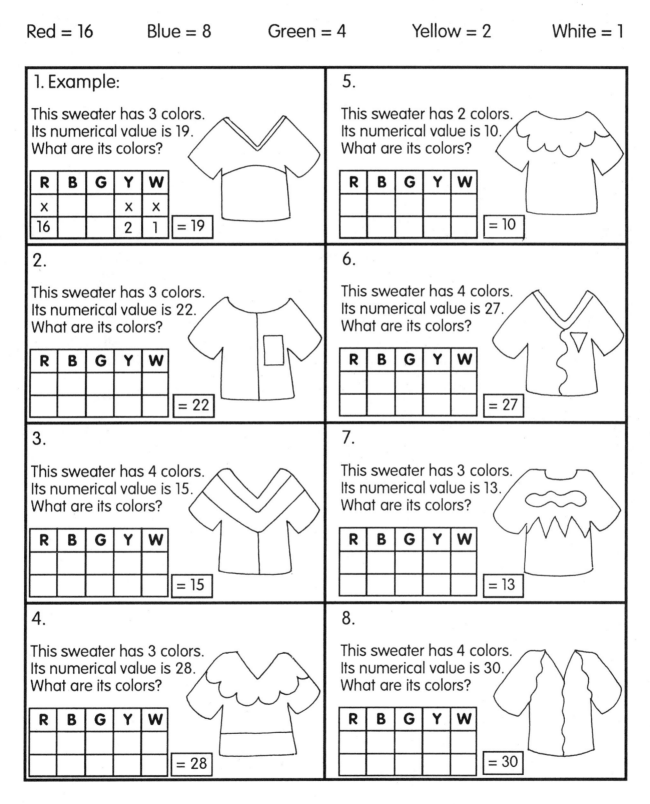

1. Example:

This sweater has 3 colors.
Its numerical value is 19.
What are its colors?

R	B	G	Y	W
x			x	x
16			2	1	= 19

5.

This sweater has 2 colors.
Its numerical value is 10.
What are its colors?

R	B	G	Y	W
					= 10

2.

This sweater has 3 colors.
Its numerical value is 22.
What are its colors?

R	B	G	Y	W
					= 22

6.

This sweater has 4 colors.
Its numerical value is 27.
What are its colors?

R	B	G	Y	W
					= 27

3.

This sweater has 4 colors.
Its numerical value is 15.
What are its colors?

R	B	G	Y	W
					= 15

7.

This sweater has 3 colors.
Its numerical value is 13.
What are its colors?

R	B	G	Y	W
					= 13

4.

This sweater has 3 colors.
Its numerical value is 28.
What are its colors?

R	B	G	Y	W
					= 28

8.

This sweater has 4 colors.
Its numerical value is 30.
What are its colors?

R	B	G	Y	W
					= 30

GA1433

State Capitals and Zoo Animals

SKILLS: Problem Solving
Computational Skills
Exponents/Binary System
Mental Math

State Capitals and Zoo Animals is an opportunity for you to tell a classmate exactly what he wrote on a separate sheet of paper even though you were not watching him when the information was being recorded. This procedure can be accomplished by using either page.

Example:
Have a classmate choose any of the listed capital cities on the State Capitals page. This person is not to disclose his/her choice to you or members of your group. Once the selection has been recorded on a sheet of paper, have the classmate fold this sheet in half. Once this is completed, have the person look at the sheet headed "State Capitals." The state capitals are listed in alphabetical order and in columns. The columns are headed by the letters **A, B, C, D, E, F.** The student who recorded the secret choice is to tell you only the column or columns in which his/her state capital choice appears.

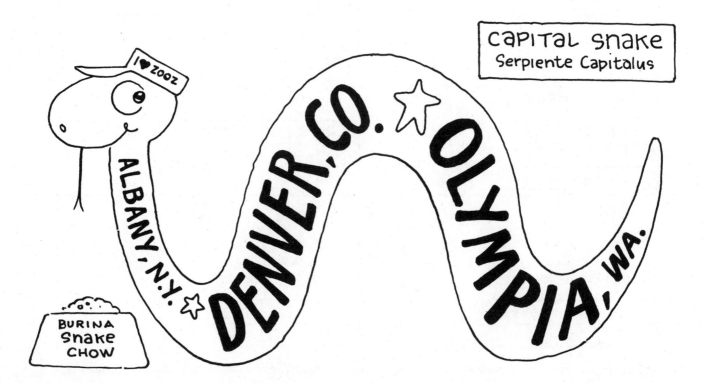

70

GA1433

State Capitals and Zoo Animals

Suppose the state capital choice is Richmond, Virginia. The classmate must tell you not his/her choice but the column or columns that this choice appears in.

"The state capital I have selected can be found in Columns A, C and F."

For you and your group to be able to identify the state capital selection, all you have to do is give a numerical value to each column heading as indicated.

A	B	C	D	E	F
32	16	8	4	2	1

In the above illustration the columns noted were A, C and F. Use the values assigned to these columns and you should come to the following conclusion:

$$\begin{array}{ccccc} A & & C & & F \\ 32 & + & 8 & + & 1 & = & 41 \end{array}$$

Now refer this number to the page titled "State Capitals" and you will see that 41 has been assigned to Richmond, Virginia.

GA1433

State Capitals

1. Albany, New York
2. Annapolis, Maryland
3. Atlanta, Georgia
4. Augusta, Maine
5. Austin, Texas
6. Baton Rouge, Louisiana
7. Bismark, North Dakota
8. Boise, Idaho
9. Boston, Massachusetts
10. Carson City, Nevada
11. Charleston, West Virginia
12. Cheyenne, Wyoming
13. Columbia, South Carolina
14. Columbus, Ohio
15. Concord, New Hampshire
16. Denver, Colorado
17. Des Moines, Iowa
18. Dover, Delaware
19. Frankfort, Kentucky
20. Harrisburg, Pennsylvania
21. Hartford, Connecticut
22. Helena, Montana
23. Honolulu, Hawaii
24. Indianapolis, Indiana
25. Jackson, Mississippi
26. Jefferson City, Missouri
27. Juneau, Alaska
28. Lansing, Michigan
29. Lincoln, Nebraska
30. Little Rock, Arkansas
31. Madison, Wisconsin
32. Montgomery, Alabama
33. Montpelier, Vermont
34. Nashville, Tennessee
35. Oklahoma City, Oklahoma
36. Olympia, Washington
37. Phoenix, Arizona
38. Pierre, South Dakota
39. Providence, Rhode Island
40. Raleigh, North Carolina
41. Richmond, Virginia
42. Sacramento, California
43. Salem, Oregon
44. Salt Lake City, Utah
45. Santa Fe, New Mexico
46. Springfield, Illinois
47. St. Paul, Minnesota
48. Tallahassee, Florida
49. Topeka, Kansas
50. Trenton, New Jersey

GA1433

State Capitals

FUTURE SITE OF HONOLULU Capital of Hawaii

A	B	C	D	E	F
Montgomery, AL	Denver, CO	Boise, ID	Augusta, ME	Annapolis, MD	Albany, NY
Montepelier, VT	Des Moines, IA	Boston, MA	Austin, TX	Atlanta, GA	Atlanta, GA
Nashville, TN	Dover, DE	Carson City, NV	Baton Rouge, LA	Baton Rouge, LA	Austin, TX
Oklahoma City, OK	Frankfort, KY	Charleston, WV	Bismark, ND	Bismark, ND	Bismark, ND
Olympia, WA	Harrisburg, PA	Cheyenne, WY	Cheyenne, WY	Carson City, NV	Boston, MA
Phoenix, AZ	Hartford, CT	Columbia, SC	Columbia, SC	Charleston, WV	Charleston, WV
Pierre, SD	Helena, MT	Columbus, OH	Columbus, OH	Columbus, OH	Columbia, SC
Providence, RI	Honolulu, HI	Concord, NH	Concord, NH	Concord, NH	Concord, NH
Raleigh, NC	Indianapolis, IN	Indianapolis, IN	Harrisburg, PA	Dover, DE	Des Moines, IA
Richmond, VA	Jackson, MS	Jackson, MS	Hartford, CT	Frankfort, KY	Frankfort, KY
Sacramento, CA	Jefferson City, MO	Jefferson City, MO	Helena, MT	Helena, MT	Hartford, CT
Salem, OR	Juneau, AK	Juneau, AK	Honolulu, HI	Honolulu, HI	Honolulu, HI
Salt Lake City, UT	Lansing, MI	Lansing, MI	Lansing, MI	Jefferson City, MO	Jackson, MS
Santa Fe, NM	Lincoln, NB	Lincoln, NB	Lincoln, NB	Juneau, AK	Juneau, AK
Springfield, IL	Little Rock, AR	Little Rock, AR	Little Rock, AR	Little Rock, AR	Lincoln, NB
St. Paul, MN	Madison, WI	Madison, WI	Madison, WI	Madison, WI	Madison, WI
Tallahassee, FL	Tallahassee, FL	Raleigh, NC	Olympia, WA	Nashville, TN	Montpelier, VT
Topeka, KS	Topeka, KS	Richmond, VA	Phoenix, AZ	Oklahoma City, OK	Oklahoma City, OK
Trenton, NJ	Trenton, NJ	Sacramento, CA	Pierre, SD	Pierre, SD	Phoenix, AZ
		Salem, OR	Providence, RI	Providence, RI	Providence, RI
		Salt Lake City, UT	Salt Lake City, UT	Sacramento, CA	Richmond, VA
		Santa Fe, NM	Santa Fe, NM	Salem, OR	Salem, OR
		Springfield, IL	Springfield, IL	Springfield, IL	Santa Fe, NM
		St. Paul, MN	St. Paul, MN	St. Paul, MN	St. Paul, MN
				Trenton, NJ	Topeka, KS

GA1433

Zoo Animals

1. anaconda
2. bear
3. bee
4. bird
5. bison
6. camel
7. cat
8. cheetah
9. chimpanzee
10. chipmunk
11. coyote
12. dog
13. dolphin
14. donkey
15. elephant
16. elk
17. fish
18. fox
19. giraffe
20. gorilla
21. horse
22. hummingbird
23. jaguar
24. kangaroo
25. lion
26. monkey
27. moose
28. mouse
29. mule
30. ostrich
31. otter
32. owl
33. parrot
34. partridge
35. pig
36. quail
37. rabbit
38. raccoon
39. sheep
40. skunk
41. squirrel
42. squid
43. tiger
44. turtle
45. vicuna
46. whale
47. wolf
48. wolverine
49. yak
50. zebra

74

A	B	C	D	E	F
owl	elk	cheetah	bird	bear	anaconda
parrot	fish	chimpanzee	bison	bee	bee
partridge	fox	chipmunk	camel	camel	bison
pig	giraffe	coyote	cat	cat	cat
quail	gorilla	dog	dog	chipmunk	chimpanzee
rabbit	horse	dolphin	dolphin	coyote	coyote
raccoon	hummingbird	donkey	donkey	donkey	dolphin
sheep	jaguar	elephant	elephant	elephant	elephant
skunk	kangaroo	kangaroo	gorilla	fox	fish
squirrel	lion	lion	horse	giraffe	giraffe
squid	monkey	monkey	hummingbird	hummingbird	horse
tiger	moose	moose	jaguar	jaguar	jaguar
turtle	mouse	mouse	mouse	monkey	lion
vicuna	mule	mule	mule	moose	moose
whale	ostrich	ostrich	ostrich	ostrich	mule
wolf	otter	otter	otter	otter	otter
wolverine	wolverine	skunk	quail	partridge	parrot
yak	yak	squirrel	rabbit	pig	pig
zebra	zebra	squid	raccoon	raccoon	rabbit
		tiger	sheep	sheep	sheep
		turtle	turtle	squid	squirrel
		vicuna	vicuna	tiger	tiger
		whale	whale	whale	vicuna
		wolf	wolf	wolf	wolf
				zebra	yak

75

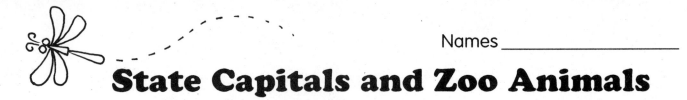

State Capitals and Zoo Animals

Use the State Capitals list to record the name of each city. To help you, your group will be given the numerical distribution. Find the sum and you will be able to record the name of the city.

	Example	A.	B.	C.	D.	E.	F.	G.	H.	I.	J.
State Capital	Indianapolis, IN										
Sum	24										
=	=	=	=	=	=	=	=	=	=	=	=
F 1			X		X	X		X	X	X	X
E 2			X		X	X	X	X	X		X
D 4			X		X				X	X	X
C 8	X		X		X	X			X	X	X
B 16	X		X	X				X	X		
A 32		X		X		X	X			X	X

Copyright © 1993, Good Apple

GA1433

State Capitals and Zoo Animals

Use the State Capitals list to discover the numerical distribution for each state capital.

State Capital	A 32	B 16	C 8	D 4	E 2	F 1	=	Sum
Example: Little Rock, AR = 30		X	X	X			=	30
A. Jackson, MS = 25								
B. Lincoln, NB = 29								
C. Trenton, NJ = 50								
D. Springfield, IL = 46								
E. Salem, OR = 43								
F. Olympia, WA = 36								
G. Lansing, MI = 28								
H. Juneau, AK = 27								
I. Pierre, SD = 38								
J. Honolulu, HI = 23								

GA1433

State Capitals and Zoo Animals

Names _____

Use the Zoo Animals list to record the numerical distribution for those animals listed in the first column.

Zoo Animals		A 32	B 16	C 8	D 4	E 2	F 1	=	Sum
Example:	parrot = 33	X					X	=	33
A.	lion = 25							=	
B.	mouse = 28							=	
C.	elephant = 15							=	
D.	partridge = 34							=	
E.	yak = 49							=	
F.	chipmunk = 10							=	
G.	mule = 29							=	
H.	turtle = 44							=	
I.	skunk = 40							=	

GA1433

Names _____

State Capitals and Zoo Animals

Use the Zoo Animals list to record the name of each animal. Your group is given the numerical distribution. Find the sum and you will find the animal.

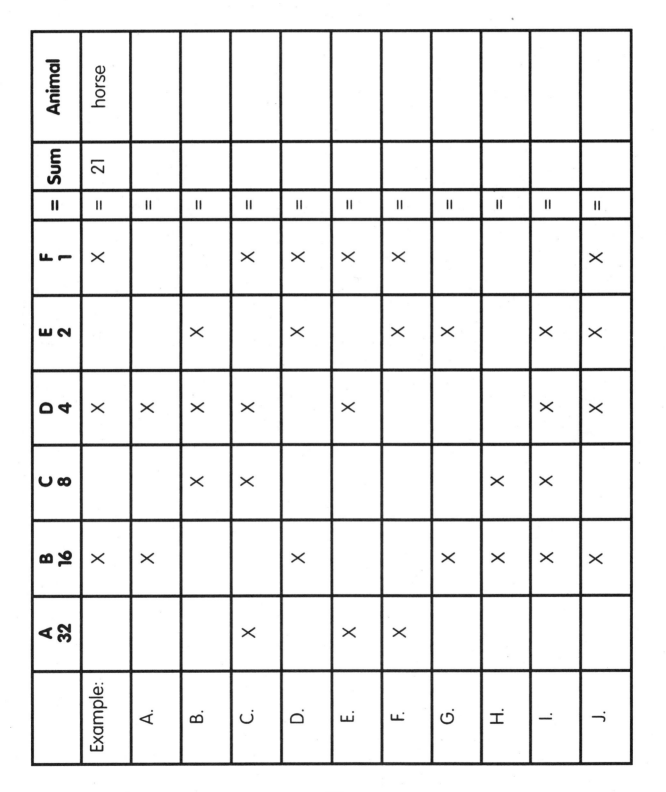

	Example	A.	B.	C.	D.	E.	F.	G.	H.	I.	J.
Animal	horse										
Sum	21										
=	=	=	=	=	=	=	=	=	=	=	=
F 1	X			X	X	X	X				X
E 2			X		X		X	X		X	X
D 4	X	X	X	X		X				X	X
C 8			X	X					X	X	
B 16	X	X			X			X	X	X	X
A 32				X		X	X				

GA1433

How Many?

SKILLS: Problem Solving
Multiplication/Division
Calculators
Fractions

| How many marbles are on each truck? |

Here is information that will help your group solve this problem.

      a. There are 30 marbles in each bag.
      b. There are 30 bags in each box.
      c. There are 30 boxes in each carton.
      d. There are 30 cartons on every truck.

      So how many marbles are on each truck?

Answers:

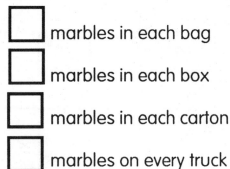

☐ marbles in each bag

☐ marbles in each box

☐ marbles in each carton

☐ marbles on every truck

Oh! By the way . . .
There are 7 trucks in the convoy. The convoy began in Cleveland, Ohio, and it is on its way to Buffalo, New York.

When the convoy reaches Buffalo, New York, it will be carrying ☐ marbles.

And that is a lot of marbles for any city!

GA1433

What If?

What if your group had a paper rectangle that measured 4" x 8"? Then suppose one day this paper rectangle was cut in half, and one half was thrown away and one half was saved.

Now on day two suppose this remaining half was cut in half. Again one half was thrown away and one half was saved.

On day three, the remaining half was cut in half.

Suppose this process continued for a total of eight days.

Question:
   If the rectangle had a value of 32 on day one, and a value of 16 on day two, what would be the value of the remaining piece of the rectangle on day eight?

day one value	=	32	day five value	=	
day two value	=	16	day six value	=	
day three value	=		day seven value	=	
day four value	=		day eight value	=	

What's in the Box?

There were 24 pieces of candy in the box.

a. Half of them contain nuts. = ☐ candies

b. One fourth of them are dark chocolate. = ☐ candies

c. Three quarters of them are milk chocolate. = ☐ candies

d. One third of them contain fruit. = ☐ candies

e. Three eights of them are my favorites. = ☐ candies

f. One sixth of the candy I didn't like at all. = ☐ candies

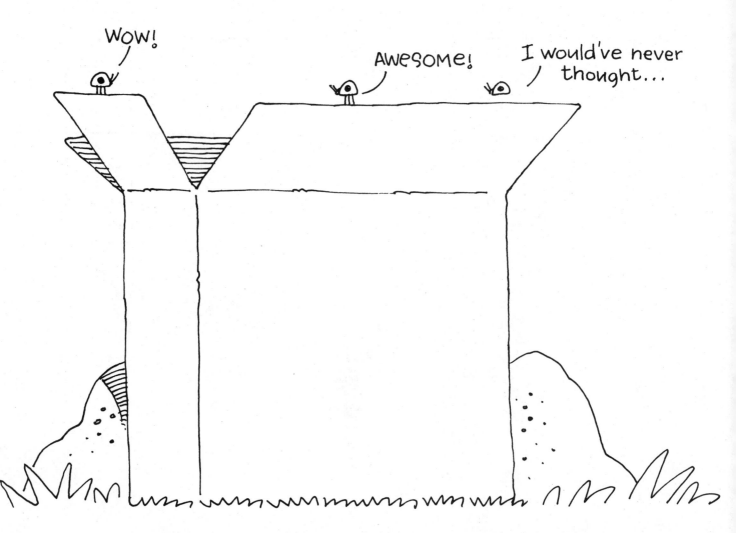

GA1433

Do We Need a Sweater?

Each of these problems has a start time. The task for your group is to determine the temperature at the conclusion of a designated time period.

---

1. The sun had been out since early morning. There was very little wind. At 9:00 a.m. the temperature in the city was 18°. For the next six hours, the temperature was noted and recorded at the end of each hour.

   Start: At 10 a.m. the temperature was 11° colder.
          11 a.m. it was 2° warmer.
          12 noon it was 7° colder.
          1 p.m. it was 3° warmer.
          2 p.m. it was 6° warmer.
          3 p.m. it was 11° colder.

   a. What was the temperature at 3 p.m.? _____

   b. Would we need a sweater? _____

---

2. At 10:00 a.m. the temperature held steady at 40°. For the next six hours, the temperature was noted and recorded at the end of each hour.

   Start: At 11 a.m. the temperature was 10° colder.
          12 noon it was 2° colder.
          1 p.m. it was 5° warmer.
          2 p.m. it was 9° colder.
          3 p.m. it was 4° warmer.
          4 p.m. it was 2° colder.

   a. What was the temperature at 4 p.m.? _____

   b. Would we need a sweater? _____

Do we need a sweater?

Is a polar bear white?

GA1433

Do We Need a Sweater?

Each of these problems has a start time. The task for your group is to determine the temperature at the conclusion of a designated time period.

---

3. When the football game began, the temperature was 42°. The game began at 2 p.m.

   Start: 42°
   > One-half hour later, it was 5° cooler.
   > One hour later, it was 4° warmer.
   > Fifteen minutes later, it was 3° warmer.
   > Two hours later, it was 11° cooler,
   > and finally, one-half hour later, it was 3° warmer.

   Two questions:
   > a. What is the temperature? _____
   > b. What is the time? _____

---

4. Can we skate on the ice yet? Skating is allowed if the temperature is 10° or below.

   Start: On Monday, 2 p.m., temperature 24°
   > Tuesday, 2 p.m., temperature 6° cooler
   > Wednesday, 2 p.m., temperature 3° warmer
   > Thursday, 2 p.m., temperature 14° cooler
   > Friday, 2 p.m., temperature 3° warmer
   > Saturday, 2 p.m., temperature 7° cooler

   On Saturday at 2 p.m.
   > a. Can we skate? _____
   > b. What is the temperature? _____

GA1433

Shade or Darken

SKILL: Number Theory

Your group is to follow directions that ask you to shade or darken specific boxes.

Upon successful completion of this task, you will discover someone's name.

A. _____

B. _____

A. Shade or darken all odd numbers.

31	27	19	44	33	16	48	8	30	50
5	42	93	14	89	74	6	66	90	20
23	63	1	46	71	4	64	88	28	4
57	40	45	18	47	53	75	54	2	32
72	20	80	70	84	34	82	30	68	14
85	29	59	2	57	62	100	10	7	52
77	86	31	56	43	71	26	98	75	18
17	99	3	12	65	24	49	92	11	6
13	60	29	96	81	94	76	33	83	40
22	78	38	58	93	36	12	50	97	10

B. Shade or darken all even numbers.

42	86	38	31	78	23	61	1	14	45
4	41	52	59	16	33	21	81	22	11
18	0	46	11	36	79	83	63	98	65
20	29	100	57	80	70	6	19	76	3
43	9	77	97	5	15	49	69	13	99
88	56	48	35	95	74	98	10	52	47
76	25	93	73	51	30	71	39	19	17
60	91	7	37	17	42	8	6	67	21
38	26	90	53	85	2	25	15	27	23
27	89	55	87	13	94	36	78	40	29

Shade number 19!

Roger

Shady Airways

GA1433

Shade or Darken

Shade or darken specific boxes and discover some-one's name.

C. _____

D. _____

C. Shade or darken all multiples of 5.

20	26	92	27	25	47	33	105	100	80
45	65	18	75	90	9	21	120	11	110
5	41	70	36	65	73	53	30	35	10
95	38	28	47	15	6	62	40	22	30
101	72	93	91	3	71	33	76	94	54
140	40	15	1	73	5	74	56	175	88
0	99	75	12	66	75	96	40	57	53
80	170	151	72	77	90	55	2	51	52
90	71	40	97	69	185	59	30	48	46
30	98	44	130	68	70	58	49	20	47

D. Shade or darken all multiples of 6.

20	99	40	102	78	18	3	132	6	96
71	27	93	50	138	17	184	24	7	85
42	84	54	43	144	38	4	126	40	32
0	98	49	65	150	83	22	60	138	120
108	12	78	105	41	17	100	104	35	11
107	145	72	95	174	48	30	1	63	106
90	102	96	100	94	18	191	15	32	182
183	70	2	28	68	36	92	90	18	66
45	14	97	31	93	54	61	174	79	72
9	22	15	74	62	92	75	36	180	12

Shade number 18!

Yes, SUH!

GA1433

Shade or Darken

Shade or darken specific boxes and discover someone's name.

E. _____

F. _____

E. Shade or darken all multiples of 5 and 6.

35	95	54	8	66	7	90	21	4	11
18	28	19	4	60	23	78	31	37	14
40	5	6	19	40	16	20	3	8	41
13	27	18	13	90	47	96	43	23	27
25	24	100	37	25	30	10	14	49	32
7	41	26	11	26	31	9	47	7	3
101	22	9	35	14	29	28	55	16	46
11	29	4	24	17	30	21	15	57	8
43	7	38	12	3	24	51	42	4	53
46	29	13	18	50	15	6	45	32	56

F. Shade or darken all multiples of 3 and 4.

7	101	42	19	34	9	52	12	103	47
13	79	36	89	23	8	101	43	77	19
9	89	24	71	97	20	18	40	17	37
4	49	32	17	14	57	41	36	37	58
60	3	30	61	38	66	28	105	38	29
13	29	22	49	2	1	89	5	83	77
6	12	16	58	29	5	10	46	39	73
33	10	27	2	19	64	26	107	53	16
56	11	44	59	67	12	22	52	5	6
39	21	48	103	53	51	40	36	21	105

Royal Bear Force

Shade number 21

Long live the Queen, Sir!

GA1433

Shade or Darken

Your group is to follow directions that ask you to shade or darken specific boxes.

Upon successful completion of this task, you will discover someone's name.

G. _____

H. _____

G. Shade or darken all prime numbers.

11	31	7	4	19	31	47	26	15	6
19	33	18	16	9	5	10	6	40	22
23	13	2	6	14	41	15	22	34	40
14	32	17	12	20	13	8	32	4	35
3	41	5	30	50	11	48	24	49	24
10	9	15	8	22	30	49	10	4	50
7	5	19	18	17	12	20	2	34	10
11	33	13	4	13	11	28	11	48	36
23	17	2	8	29	16	31	37	4	6
37	35	43	14	43	50	36	47	12	18

H. Shade or darken all prime numbers.

37	5	11	20	47	23	3	8	33	10
31	46	23	15	11	20	31	9	4	34
3	17	19	6	29	47	13	49	10	14
5	50	4	12	5	30	17	26	33	16
41	22	32	22	2	4	7	40	24	8
49	14	9	40	14	8	18	6	49	10
4	41	12	24	29	35	11	16	4	42
50	43	6	10	5	15	19	30	34	15
22	47	32	42	23	18	37	28	40	50
40	19	2	3	11	35	43	41	13	2

GA1433

Shade or Darken

The two grids are provided for your group.

Create your own name puzzle and pass it on to another group.

I. _____

J. _____

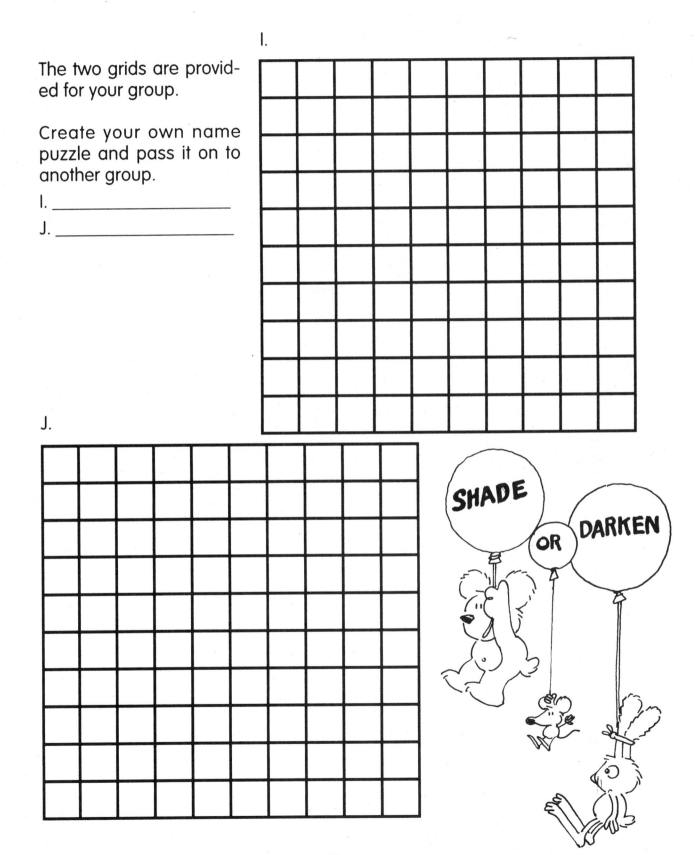

GA1433

Prime Primes

SKILLS: Prime Numbers
Problem Solving

Prime numbers less than 30 are recorded in the rectangle. The objective of the activity is to have your group reach as many of the sums listed on the work sheet; however, you want to reach this sum by using the least number of primes.

2	3	5	7	11	13	17	19	23	29

Example:
Reach the sum of 9 using prime numbers.

$$5 + 2 + 2 = 9$$

However, the answer can be reached with less primes.

$$7 + 2 = 9$$

Another example:
Reach the sum of 12 using prime numbers.

$$7 + 3 + 2 = 12$$

However, the answer can be reached with less primes.

$$7 + 5 = 12$$

FROM NEW YORK! IT'S PRIME PRIMES LIVE!

GA1433

Prime Primes

Your group is to try to reach each sum by using the least number of primes.
The primes that may be used are below.

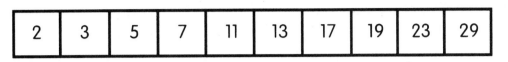

| 2 | 3 | 5 | 7 | 11 | 13 | 17 | 19 | 23 | 29 |

Be sure to discuss your answers. They may vary.

a.	b.	c.
= 10	= 18	= 22
d.	e.	f.
= 25	= 15	= 16
g.	h.	i.
= 21	= 26	= 14

GA1433

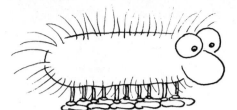

Prime Primes

Your group is to try to reach each sum by using the least number of primes. The primes that may be used are

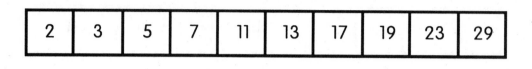

| 2 | 3 | 5 | 7 | 11 | 13 | 17 | 19 | 23 | 29 |

j.

= 24

k.

= 30

l.

= 28

m.

= 27

n.

= 32

o.

= 19

p.

= 34

q.

= 23

r.

= 33

GA1433

Wordsworth I

SKILLS: Place Value
        Expanded Notation
        Addition

When you consider the sentence The sky is blue. , a picture of a large blue sky may come to mind.

However, for this activity your group might want to put a somewhat different picture in their mind. If you try extra hard, the same statement The sky is blue. just might put a number in your mind. The number in mind just might be 1210.

This could be in mind if you take the words in the sentence and distribute them according to the number of letters in each word as well as considering the concept of place value.

4-Letter Words	3-Letter Words	2-Letter Words	1-Letter Words
thousands	hundreds	tens	ones
blue	The	is	
	sky		

Blue placed in the thousands column =   1000

The and sky placed in the hundreds column =   200

is placed in the tens column =   10
              added together =   1210

The sky is blue. = 1210

The sky is blue.

...and there's a leak in your boat.

GA1433

Wordsworth I

Another example:

| Her dog is very, very nice to me. |

The number value of this sentence can be found by placing each word in the column headed by the number of letters in each word. Follow this procedure by totaling the amount of each column.

4-Letter Words	3-Letter Words	2-Letter Words	1-Letter Words
thousands	hundreds	tens	ones
very	her	is	
very	dog	to	
nice		me	

| very | + | very | + | nice | = | 3000 |

| Her | + | dog | | | = | 200 |

| is | + | to | + | me | = | 30 |

added together = 3230

| Her dog is very, very nice to me. | = 3230

Her dog is
very, very
nice to
me.

Not to
me.

GA1433

Wordsworth I

Record the words of the sentence in the proper columns. When all of the words are recorded, determine the number value of the sentence according to place value.

1. | She is very glad to buy a new book. |

4-Letter Words	3-Letter Words	2-Letter Words	1-Letter Words
thousands	hundreds	tens	ones

Work space

| She is very glad to buy a new book. | = | |

GA1433

Wordsworth I

Record the words of the sentence in the proper columns. When all of the words are recorded, determine the number value of the sentence according to place value.

2. | When will John and Sue ever see a tiny goat?

4-Letter Words	3-Letter Words	2-Letter Words	1-Letter Words
thousands	hundreds	tens	ones

Work space

When will John and Sue ever see a tiny goat? = _____

GA1433

Wordsworth II

SKILLS: Place Value
        Expanded Notation
        Addition

Wordsworth II is the opposite of Wordsworth I. This activity asks your group to begin with a number and conclude with a sentence. The number of letters in each word is to match its position according to place value.

Example: 3211

This number lets you know that the sentence in question has seven words in it.

Three of the words contain four letters according to place value.	<u>3</u>211
Two of the words contain three letters according to place value.	3<u>2</u>11
One word contains two letters according to place value.	32<u>1</u>1
One word contains one letter according to place value.	321<u>1</u>

Read the sentence below and decide if the above statements are true.

> Mike and Andy are at a show.

Of course many other sentences with seven words will fit this configuration.

Mike and Andy are at a show.

It's Sunday... they're supposed to be at the bird sanctuary!

GA1433

Wordsworth II

The number in each box tells you about the sentence your group is to create. The number indicates the number of words in each sentence as well as the number of letters in each word.

Your group is to create sentences for the following numbers. In this activity, the sharing of ideas is very helpful.

1.

The value of the sentence is 5100.

2.

The value of the sentence is 4120.

3.

The value of the sentence is 1240.

GA1433

If . . .

SKILLS: Problem Solving
       Patterning
       Calculators
       Multiplication/Division
       Word Problems

Here are some "Ifs" for your group to consider. As your group uses various strategies to reach solutions to the "If" problems, they will find a calculator a most useful aid.

a. If you ate an apple a day, how many years would it take to eat . . .

       1095 apples? ☐ years
       2190 apples? ☐ years
       5475 apples? ☐ years

b. If you ate an apple a day, how long must you live to eat a million apples? (It would help to turn days into years.)

       ☐ years

c. If there were five members in your group, and you all loved apples, and you all ate an apple a day, how many years would it take for the five group members to eat a million apples?

       ☐ years

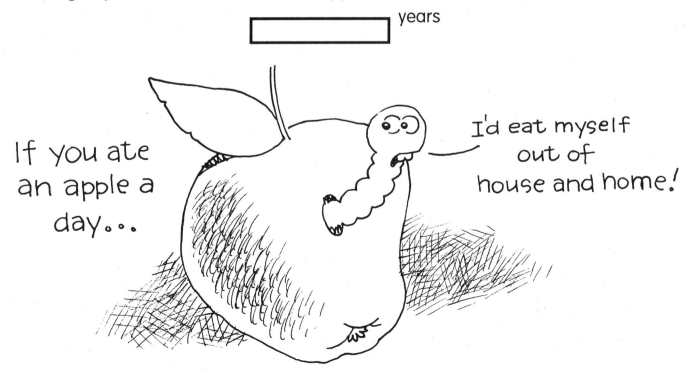

If you ate an apple a day...

I'd eat myself out of house and home!

GA1433

If . . .

Additional "If" problems. Remember the calculator will be most helpful in solving these problems.

d. If you were able to save a penny a day, how much money would you have in

1 year?	
5 years?	
10 years?	
21 years?	

e. If the five members in your group each saved a penny a day, how much money would your group save in

1 year?	
5 years?	
10 years?	
34 years?	

Please share the methods you used with the other groups. How did you arrive at your answers?

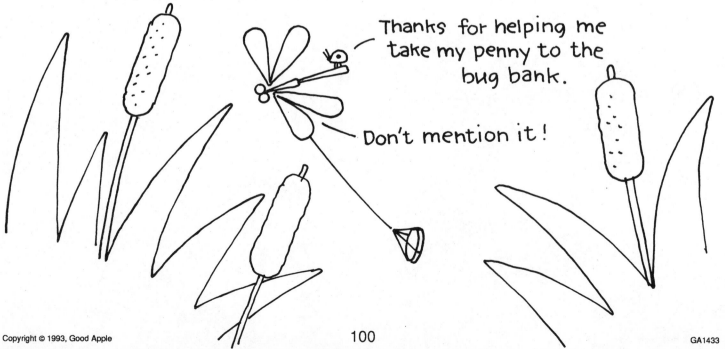

Thanks for helping me take my penny to the bug bank.

Don't mention it!

If . . .

More "If" problems. Don't forget the calculator!

f. If the members of your group each saved a different amount of money each day and if there were five people in the group and if one member saved a penny a day, the second member saved two pennies a day, the third member saved three pennies a day, the fourth member saved four pennies every day and the fifth and last group member saved five pennies every day, how long would it take for your group to collectively save

$1000? ☐

$10,000? ☐

$50,000? ☐

Share your thoughts and ideas as to how you arrived at the answers.

g. If you were old enough to buy an automobile and the automobile had a price tag of $12,000 and you were going to pay for it with pennies, what might this scene look like?

Share this with your team members. Listen to their thoughts and ideas.

The If Skiff

If . . .

The following "If" problems deal with the concept of time. The calculator will be most helpful in the solution of the problems.

h. If someone asked how many seconds in an hour?

There are _____ seconds in one hour.

Solve the following:

_____ seconds in ten hours

_____ seconds in one day

_____ seconds in two days

_____ seconds in one week

i. If someone asked

how many seconds in one month (thirty days)?_____

how many seconds in two months?_____

how many seconds in one year?_____

how many seconds in two years?_____

*How many seconds old are you?

Share your method of reaching the solution!

Answer Key

Poems Pages 2-4

Geese, Page 2

1. 24		3. 3	
2. 12		4. 1	

School Yard, Page 3

1. 6		3. 8	
2. 12		4. 4	

The Mystery Book, Page 4

1. Monday = $1.20
2. Wednesday = $7.20
3. Thursday and Friday = $10.80
4. Book cost = $10.80

How Many Animals in My Zoo?
I'll Tell You! Page 5

220 animals

Cross Out Something Pages 7-9

Page 7	Page 9
A = 11	E = 32, 35 or 31, 36
B = 21	F = 52, 39
Page 8	
C = 23	
D = 22, 70	

This Is Really, Really, Odd! Page 12

A	B	C	D	=	Sum
3	4	5	1	=	13
5	6	4	2	=	17
1	3	9	6	=	19
4	5	6	8	=	23
8	9	3	5	=	25
7	8	2	0	=	17
0	2	1	4	=	7

This Is the Challenge! These Are
the Facts Pages 13-17

Page 13

Sally is 12 years old.
Sam is 18 years old.
Sue is 3 years old.
Serena is 6 years old.
Sonny is 9 years old.

Page 14

Mark read 17 books.
Robyn read 10 books.
Dawn read 6 books.
Michele read 12 books.
Alan read 9 books.

Page 15

46 sharks in tank.
92 sea bass in tank.
184 flounder in tank.
190 fluke in tank.
23 stingrays in tank.

Page 16

3 toy stores
11 restaurants
6 shoe stores
12 clothing stores
4 electronic centers
4 bookstores

Page 17

Todd has 258 baseball cards.
Theresa has 127 baseball cards.
Terrence has 124 baseball cards.
Timmy has 86 baseball cards.
Tyler has 172 baseball cards.
Collectively there are 767 cards.

What Did You Say to Your Mom?
Page 20

Day	Number of Responses
1	2
2	4
3	8
4	16
5	32
10	1024
20	1,048,576

Making "Pals" Pages 27-28

Page 27

A. Take 2 steps. The palindrome is 4664.
B. Take 5 steps. The palindrome is 59895.
C. Take 3 steps. The palindrome is 15851.
D. Take 5 steps. The palindrome is 44044.

GA1433

Page 28
E. Take 3 steps. The palindrome is 2992.
F. Take 3 steps. The palindrome is 7337.
G. Take 8 steps. The palindrome is 1136311.

Which "Pal" Is Closest? Page 31
A. 585–addition
B. 868–subtraction
C. 252–addition
D. 313 or 303–addition or subtraction

Even Steven Pages 33-35
Page 33

	Players	Cards
24 cards	1	24
	2	12
	3	8
	4	6
	6	4
	8	3
	12	2
	24	1

Page 34

	Players	Cards
36 cards	1	36
	2	18
	3	12
	4	9
	6	6
	9	4
	12	3
	18	2
	36	1

	Players	Cards
52 cards	1	52
	2	26
	4	13
	13	4
	26	2
	52	1

Page 35

	Players	Cards
56 cards	1	56
	2	28
	4	14
	7	8
	8	7
	14	4
	28	2
	56	1

	Players	Cards
100 cards	1	100
	2	50
	4	25
	5	20
	10	10
	20	5
	25	4
	50	2
	100	1

Identification Problems Pages 38-40
Page 38
A. 3 pennies
   2 dimes
B. 4 nickels
   2 quarters
Page 39
C. 7 pennies
   3 quarters
D. 6 dimes
   2 quarters
Page 40
E. 3 dimes
   3 quarters
F. 1 dime
   6 quarters

Match Me! Page 47
A. Initial letters match
B. Initial letters match
C. Colors associated with food words
   yellow   banana
   red   apple
   white   milk
   blue   berry
D. Initial letters match

GA1433

E. Color words match the number of letters in the animals

yellow	rabbit
red	yak
white	moose
blue	fish

F. Colors match numbers (10 x + 1)

yellow	(10 x 6) + 1 = 61
red	(10 x 3) + 1 = 31
white	(10 x 5) + 1 = 51
blue	(10 x 4) + 1 = 41

G. Color match number of letters times 3

yellow	(6 x 3) = 18
red	(3 x 3) = 9
white	(5 x 3) = 15
blue	(4 x 3) = 12

H. Colors match the number of letters in the color word

yellow	six
red	three
white	five
blue	four

I. Colors match the number of letters times itself

yellow	(6 x 6) = 36
red	(3 x 3) = 9
white	(5 x 5) = 25
blue	(4 x 4) = 16

J. Colors match the number of letters in the color word. This number can be found in the tens column.

yellow = 6	7160
red = 3	2130
white = 5	50
blue = 4	140

Column A or Column B? Pages 49-50
Page 49
1. Square numbers
2. Numbers constructed by straight lines only
3. Numbers with 2's in them
4. Number words beginning with the letter **S**

Page 50
5. Number words with three letters
6. Number words that can be used as words
7. Number words with two syllables
8. Prime numbers less than 20

Sweater Time, Pages 68-69
Page 68
2. 8 + 4 + 1 = 13
3. 16 + 8 + 1 = 25
4. 16 + 8 + 4 + 2 = 30
5. 16 + 8 + 4 = 28
6. 4 + 2 + 1 = 7
7. 16 + 1 = 17
8. 16 + 4 + 1 = 21

Page 69
2. red, green, yellow
3. blue, green, yellow, white
4. red, blue, green
5. blue, yellow
6. red, blue, yellow, white
7. blue, green, white
8. red, blue, green, yellow

State Capitals and Zoo Animals, Pages 76-79
Page 76
A. 33, Montpelier, VT
B. 30, Little Rock, AR
C. 49, Topeda, KS
D. 15, Concord, NH
E. 42, Sacramento, CA
F. 35, Oklahoma City, OK
G. 19, Frankfort, KY
H. 31, Madison, WI
I. 45, Santa Fe, NM
J. 47, St. Paul, MN

Page 77
A. 16 + 8 + 1 = 25
B. 16 + 8 + 4 + 1 = 29
C. 32 + 16 + 2 = 50
D. 32 + 8 + 4 + 2 = 46
E. 32 + 8 + 2 + 1 = 43
F. 32 + 4 = 36
G. 16 + 8 + 4 = 28
H. 16 + 8 + 2 + 1 = 27
I. 32 + 4 + 2 = 38
J. 16 + 4 + 2 + 1 = 23

Page 78
A. 16 + 8 + 1 = 25
B. 16 + 8 + 4 = 28
C. 8 + 4 + 2 + 1 = 15
D. 32 + 2 = 34
E. 32 + 16 + 1 = 49
F. 8 + 2 = 10
G. 16 + 8 + 4 + 1 = 29
H. 32 + 8 + 4 = 44
I. 32 + 8 = 40

GA1433

Page 79
A. 20, gorilla
B. 14, donkey
C. 45, vicuna
D. 19, giraffe
E. 37, rabbit
F. 35, pig
G. 18, fox
H. 24, kangaroo
I. 30, ostrich
J. 23, jaguar

How Many? Page 80
30 marbles in each bag
900 marbles in each box
27,000 marbles in each carton
810,000 marbles in each truck
5,670,000 marbles in convoy

What If? Page 81
day one = 32
day two = 16
day three = 8
day four = 4
day five = 2
day six = 1
day seven = .50
day eight = .25

What's in the Box? Page 82
a. 12 candies with nuts
b. 6 candies with dark chocolate
c. 18 candies with milk chocolate
d. 8 candies with fruit
e. 9 candies are my favorites
f. 4 candies I did not like

Do We Need a Sweater? Pages 83-84
Page 83
1. a. 0°
   b. yes
2. a. 26°
   b. yes

Page 84
3. a. 36°
   b. 6:15 p.m.
4. a. yes
   b. 3°

Shade or Darken Pages 85-88
Page 85
A. Alan
B. Alice
Page 86
C. Mark
D. Scott

Page 87
E. Sue
F. José
Page 88
G. Stan
H. Paul

Prime Primes Pages 91-92
Page 91
a. 7 + 3 = 10
b. 13 + 5 = 18 or 7 + 11 = 18
c. 17 + 5 = 22 or 3 + 19 = 22
d. 23 + 2 = 25
e. 13 + 2 = 15
f. 11 + 5 = 16
g. 19 + 2 = 21

h. 19 + 7 = 26 or 3 + 23 = 26
i. 11 + 3 = 14
Page 92
j. 17 + 7 = 24 or 5 + 19 = 24
k. 23 + 7 = 30 or 13 + 17 = 30
l. 23 + 5 = 28 or 11 + 17 = 28
m. 17 + 7 + 3 = 27 or 19 + 5 + 3 = 27
n. 29 + 3 = 32 or 13 + 19 = 32
o. 17 + 2 = 19
p. 23 + 11 = 34 or 5 + 29 = 34
q. 19 + 2 + 2 = 23
r. 23 + 7 + 3 = 33

Wordworth I Pages 95-96
Page 95
1. 3321
Page 96
2. 6301

If . . . Pages 99-102
Page 99
a. 3 years
   6 years
   15 years
b. 2740 years
c. 548 years
Page 100
d. $3.65
   $18.25
   $36.50
   $76.65
e. $18.25
   $91.25
   $182.50
   $620.50
Page 101
f. five members in the group
   A, B, C, D, E
   A saves $3.65
   B saves $7.30
   C saves $10.95
   D saves $14.60
   E saves $18.25
            $54.75 a year
$1000 about 18 years
$10,000 about 182 years
$50,000 about 913 years
Page 102
h. 3600 seconds in one hour
   36,000 seconds in ten hours
   86,400 seconds in one day
   172,800 seconds in two days
   604,800 seconds in one week
i. 2,592,000 seconds in one month
   5,184,000 seconds in two months
   31,104,000 seconds in one year
   62,208,000 seconds in two years

GA1433